OPERATIC ANTHOLOGY

CELEBRATED ARIAS
Selected from
OPERAS
by
Old and Modern Composers

Compiled by
Kurt Adler

IN FIVE VOLUMES

Vol. I Soprano
Vol. II. Mezzo-Soprano and Alto
Vol. III Tenor
Vol. IV. Baritone
Vol. V. Bass

Ed. 551

New York G.Schirmer

Printed in the U. S. A.
16362

CONTENTS

CONTENTS

Re dell' abisso affrettati

Invocation Aria
from "Un Ballo in Maschera"

English version by
Charles Lamb Kenney

Giuseppe Verdi
(1813 - 1901)

fol - go-re il tet - - to mi - - o pe-ne
maj - es-ty, this my dwell - ing to en -
tra. O-mai tre vol - te
ter! Thrice hath the owl's loud
l'u - - pu-pa dal-l'al - - to so - spi -
screech - ing voice re-sound - - ed from yon
rò; la sa-la-mar - dra-i-
caves; leap - ing, the sal - - a-
pp
pp
pp

gni - vo-ra tre vol - te si - bi -
man - der thrice hath hissed through fier - y
lò... e del - le tom - be il
waves, and thrice a moan that
ge - mi-to tre vol - te a me par -
chilled like ice hath sighed from new - - - dug
f
pp
lò, e del - le tom - be il
graves! thrice, too, a moan that
f
pp

ff
ge - - mi-to tre vol - - te a me par-
chilled like ice hath sighed from new-dug
ff
pp
lò, tre vol-te a me, a me par - lò!
graves, hath sighed, hath sighed, from new-dug graves!
È
'Tis
pp
ff
Andante ♩= 100
lui! è lui! ne' pal - pi-ti co - me ri-sen-to a-
he! 'tis he! my heart a-pace beats with fierce glow-ing
pp
des - so la vo-lut-tà ri - ar - de-re
pleas - ure as of his dread yet loved em-brace

del suo tre-men-do am-ples - so!
I feel the might - y pres - sure!
La fa - ce del fu - tu - ro
A torch the fu - ture light - ing,
pp
ff
6
nel-la si-ni-stra e-gli ha.
he bears in his left hand,
M'ar - ri - se al mio scon-
his fa - vor my prayer re-
pp
f
giu - ro, ri-fol - go-rar la fa:
quit - ing, all things re-vealed now stand:
ff
f
sotto voce
nul - la, più nul - la, più nul - la a-
naught now, no, naught now, no, naught now
pppp
pp

p
cresc.
scon-der-si al guar-do mi - o po -
can be-fall, naught can be-fall but
p
cresc.
trà, nul - la a -
by my vi - sion
ff
ancora ppp
scon - - - der-si po-trà, nul - la, più
scanned, my vi-sion scanned; naught now, no,
ff
ppp
pp
p
cresc.
nul - la, più nul-la a-scon-der-si po - -
naught now, no, naught now can be-fall but
p
cresc.

trà, nul - la a -
by my vi - sion
ff
scon - - - der-si po-trà, nul-la a-scon-der-si
scanned, my vi-sion scanned; all that can be-fall
ppp
f
al guar-do mio po-trà! Si-len -
is by my vi-sion scanned! Now si -
pp
zio! si-len - zio!
lence! Now si - lence!

Una voce poco fa

Cavatina

from "Il Barbiere di Siviglia"

English version by
Natalia Macfarren

Gioacchino Rossini
(1792-1868)

Rosina
U - na vo - ce po - co fa qui nel cor mi ri - suo - nò, il mio
There's a voice that I en-shrine In_ my heart, and none must know; Ah, Lin-
p
cor_ fe - ri - to è già, e_ Lin - dor_ fu che il pia - gò. Sì, Lin-
dor,_ that voice is thine, 'Tis for thee_ my heart doth glow, Yes, Lin-
do - ro_ mio sa - rà, lo_ giu - ra - i, la_ vin - ce -
do - ro_ shall be_mine, I_ have sworn it, for_ weal or_
f
p
rò, sì, Lin - do - ro_ mio_ sa - rà, lo giu -
woe, Yes, Lin - do - ro_ shall_ be_ mine, I have_
f
p

ra - i, la — vin - ce - rò. Il tu-tor ri-cu-se-
sworn it, for weal or — woe. My in-tent I'll not re-
p
rò, io l'in-ge-gno a-guz-ze-rò, al-la fin s'ac-che-te-
sign, Though my guard-ian should say no, He my love need not di-
rà, e con-ten-ta io re-ste-rò. Sì, Lin-do - ro — mio sa-
vine, Till my hand I may be-stow. Yes, Lin-do - ro — shall be-
f
rà, lo — giu - ra - i, la — vin - ce - rò, sì, Lin-
mine, I — have sworn it, for — weal or — woe, Yes, Lin-
p

do - ro — mio — sa - rà, lo giu - ra - i, la vin-ce-rò!
do - ro — shall be — mine, I have — sworn it, for weal or woe!
f
p
Moderato
p
3
tr
f
p
f

p
Io so - no do - ci - le, son ri - spet -
I am all gen - tle-ness, I'm all de -
p
to - sa, so - no ob - be - dien - te,
vo - tion, Hum - ble, o - be - dient,
dol ce a - mo - ro - sa, mi la-scio reg - ge - re, mi la-scio
all soft e - mo - tion; I can be ruled with ease, I can be
reg - ge - re, mi fo gui - dar, mi fo gui - dar. Ma se mi
ruled with ease, nor gui-dance spurn, nor gui - dance spurn. But if you

toc - ca-no dov' è il mio de - bo-le, sa-rò u-na vi - pe - ra, sa -
cross my will, or what I do take ill, Like an-y vi - per I will
p
rò, e cen - to trap - po - le pri - ma di
turn; A thou - sand tricks I'll play, but I will
ce - de-re fa - rò gio - car, fa - rò gio - car, e cen - to
have my way, This all must learn, this all must learn; a thou-sand
trap - po - le pri-ma di ce - de-re fa - rò gio - car, fa - rò gio -
tricks I'll play, but I will have my way, this all must learn, this all must
col canto
a tempo

car, e_cen-to trap-po-le pri-ma di ce-de-re, e cen-to
learn, a_thou-sand tricks I'll play, but I_ will have my way, a thou-sand
col canto
a tempo
a piacere
trap-po - le fa - rò, fa - rò gio -
tricks I'll play, but I will have my
car!
way!
Io so-no
I am all
p
do-ci-le,
gen-tle-ness,
so-no ob-be-
all soft e-
cresc.

dien-te, mi la-scio reg-ge-re, mi fo gui-dar.
mo-tion, I can be ruled with ease, nor gui-dance spurn.
f
Ma se mi toc-ca-no dov' è il mio de-bo-le, sa-rò u-na
But if you cross my will, or what I do take ill, like an-y
col canto
p
vi-pe-ra, sa-rò, e cen-to trap-po-le pri-ma di
vi-per I will turn; A thou-sand tricks I'll play, but I will
ce-de-re fa-rò gio-car, fa-rò gio-car, e cen-to
have my way, This all must learn, this all must learn, a thou-sand

trap - po - le pri - ma di ce - de - re fa - rò gio - car, fa - rò gio -
tricks I'll play, but I will have my way, this all must learn, this all must
col canto
a tempo
car, e cen - to trap - po - le pri - ma di ce - de - re, e cen - to
learn, a thou - sand tricks I'll play, but I will have my way, a thou - sand
col canto
a tempo
a piacere
Più allegro
trap - po - le fa - rò fa - rò gio - car, e cen - to
tricks I'll play, but I will have my way, a thou - sand
f
trap - po - le fa - rò gio - car, e cen - to trap - po - le fa - rò gio -
tricks I'll play, to have my way, thou - sands of tricks I'll play to have my

car, fa - rò gio - car, fa - rò gio -
way, to have my way, to have my
car,— fa - rò gio - car!
way,— to— have my way!
f
ff

Marina's Aria

from "Boris Godunov"

Transliteration by
Anna Heifetz

Modest Mussorgsky
(1839-1881)

Poco più animato
Но лишь, тамъ въ ту - ман - ной да - ли зорь - ка яс - на - я блес - ну - ла;
No lish tam vtu - man - noi da - li zor' - ka yas - na - ya bles - nu - la;
Yet, at last, the dawn is break - ing, in the East a rose is blush - ing;
то Мос - ков - скій про - хо - ди - мецъ пан - нѣ Мни - шекъ при - гля - нул - ся.
to Mos - kov - ski pro - kho - di - metz pan - nye Mni - shek pri - glya - nul - sya.
There's a youth late come from Mos - cow who has set my heart a - beat - ing.
Tempo I
Мой Ди - мит - рій, мсти - тель гроз - ный, мсти - тель без - по - щад - ный,
Moi Di - mit - rii, msti - tel' groz - nyi msti - tel' bez - po - shchad - nyi,
My Di - mi - tri, sent by Heav - en, pit - i - less a - ven - ger,
dolce
Бо - жій судъ и Божь - я ка - ра, за ца - ре - ви -
Bo - zhii sud i Bozh' - ya ka - ra, za tza - re - vi -
God's re - dress - er, called and cho - sen, Thou shalt wreak a

poco cresc.
ча ма-лют - ку, жерт-ву влас - ти не-на-сыт-ной, жерт-ву алч - нос-
cha ma-lyut - ku zhërt-vu vlas - ti ne-na-syt-noĭ, zhërt-vu alch - nos-
time-ly ven - geance on Bor-is, the black u-surp-er Who to slake his
poco cresc.
ти Бо-ри - са, жерт-ву зло - бы Го-ду-но-ва. Раз-бу-жу же
ti Bo-ri - sa, zhert-vu zlo - by Go-du-no-va. Raz-bu-zhu-zhe
thirst for pow - er slew the in - no-cent Tsar-e-vich. I will rouse our
mf
mf
я маг-на-товъ сон - ныхъ, блес-комъ зла - та за-ма-ню я
ya mag-na-tov son - nykh, bles-kom zla - ta za-ma-nyu ya
sleep-y mag-nates, bid them fight; With the gleam of gold I'll win them
mf
Meno mosso ♩=120
шлях - ту. А те-бя, мой са - мо-зва-нецъ, мой лю-бов-никъ
slyakh - tu. A te-bya, moi sa - mo-zva-nëtz, moi lyu-bov-nik
for thy cause. As for thee, my young pre-tend-er, thou my bashful
p

том - ный, о - по - ю те - бя сле - за - ми страс - ти
tom - nyĭ, O - po - yu te - bya sle - za - mi stras - ti
woo - er, Thou shalt be en - tranced by pas - sion, mad with
жгу - чей. За - ду - шу те - бя въ объ-ять-яхъ, за - цѣ - лу - ю,
zhgu - cheĭ. Za - du - shu te - bya vob yat'-yakh, za - tze - lu - yu,
love. I will sti - fle all thy scru - ples with my ar - dent
ми - лый, мой ца - ре - вичъ, мой Ди - мит - рий, мой же - нихъ на - зван - ный.
mi - lyĭ, moĭ tza - re - vich, moĭ Di - mit - rii, Moĭ zhe - nikh na - zvan - nyĭ.
kiss - es, My Tsar - e - vich, my Di - mi - tri, long ex - pect - ed lov - er.
Нѣж - нымъ ле - пе - томъ лю - бов - нымъ слухъ твой о - ча - ру - ю,
Nezh - nym le - pe - tom lyu - bov - nym slukh troĭ o - cha - ru - yu,
I will charm thy ears with love words pas - sion - ate and ten - der,

Мой ца-ре - вичъ, мой Ди-мит-рий, мой лю-бов-никъ том - ный!
Moĭ tza-re - vich, moĭ Di-mit-riĭ, moĭ lyu-bov-nik tom - nyĭ!
My Tsar-e - vich, my Di-mi-tri, I will teach thee cour - age!
Poco più lento
Пан-нѣ Мни-шекъ слиш-комъ скуч-ны страс-ти том - ной из - лі янь - я,
Pan-nye Mni-shek slish-kom skuch-ny stras-ti tom-noĭ iz - li-yan - ya,
For Ma-ri - na long has wear-ied, sought by lov-ers shy and tep-id,
пыл-кихъ ю - но-шей мо-лень-я, рѣ-чи пош - лы - я маг-на - товъ.
pyl-kikh yu - no-sheĭ mo-len' ya re-chi posh - ly - ya mag-na - tov.
Youths who on - ly dream of pas-sion, worth-y mag-nates vain and pom-pous.
poco cresc.
Animando
Пан-на Мни-шекъ сла-вы хо-четъ, пан-на Мни-шекъ влас-ти жаж-детъ!
Pan-na Mni-shek sla-vy kho-chet, pan-na Mni-shek vlas-ti zhazh-det!
But Ma-ri - na longs for glo - ry, but Ma-ri - na craves for pow - er!

Tempo I (alla Mazurka) ♩= 144
На прес-толъ ца - рей мос-ков - скихъ
Na pres-tol tza - reĭ mos-kov - skikh
On the roy - al throne of Mos - cow
я ца - ри - цей ся - ду, и въ пор-фи - рѣ зла - то-ткан-ной
ya tza - ri - tzeĭ sya - du, i vpór-fi - rye zla - to - tkan-noĭ
I would queen it proud - ly, robed in pur - ple, decked with jew-els,
солн-цемъ за - блис - та - ю, и сра-жу кра - сой чу-дес - ной
soln-tzem za - blis - ta - yu, i sra-zhu kra - soĭ chu-des - noĭ
glit-t'ring like the sun - light, While, a-stound-ed at my beau - ty,
я мос-ка - лей ту - по-ум - ныхъ, и ста-да бо - яръ кич-ли - выхъ
ya mos-ka - leĭ tu - po-um - nykh, i sta-da bo - yar kich-li - vykh
all the sil - ly folk of Mos - cow, all the herd of boast-ful no - bles

Poco acceler.
Scherzando
бить че-ломъ се-бѣ за-став-лю. И про-сла-вятъ
bit' che-lom se-bye za-stav-lyu. I pro-sla-vyat
at my feet would fall and grov-el. In the leg-ends
p
въ сказ-кахъ, бы-ляхъ, не-бы-ли-цахъ гор-ду-ю сво-ю ца-ри-цу
vskaz-kakh, by-lyakh, ne-by-li-tzakh gor-du-yu svo-yu tza-ri-tzu
and the folk-songs would my splen-dor be re-cord-ed, At the glo-ry
p
cresc.
ту-по-ум-ны-е мос-ка-ли. Ха ха ха ха ха ха ха ха ха ха ха
tu-po-um-ny-ye mos-ka-li. Kha-kha-kha-kha-kha-kha-kha-kha-kha-kha-kha-
of Ma-ri-na men shall mar-vel! Ha! ha! ha! ha! ha! ha! ha! ha! ha! ha! ha!
f
ха! ха ха ха ха ха ха ха ха ха ха!
kha! kha-kha-kha-kha-kha-kha-kha-kha-kha-kha!
ha! ha! ha! ha! ha! ha! ha! ha! ha! ha! ha!
pp
poco cresc.
tr
f

L'amour est un oiseau rebelle

Habanera

from "Carmen"

English version by
Dr. Theodore Baker

Georges Bizet
(1838 - 1875)

Allegretto quasi Andantino ♩=72

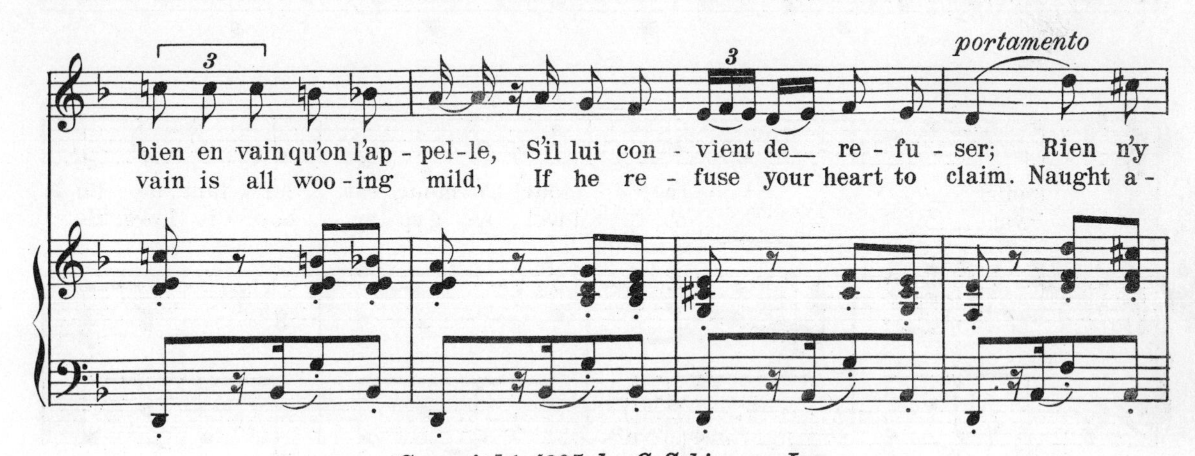

portamento
fait, menace ou pri - è - re, L'un par - le bien, l'au-tre se tait; Et c'est
vails, nei - ther threat nor prayer, One speaks me fair, the oth - er sighs, 'Tis the
l'au-tre que je pré - fè - re, Il n'a rien dit, mais il me plaît.
oth - er that I pre - fer, Though mute, his heart to mine re - plies.
espress.
L'a - mour! l'a - mour! l'a -
Oh, love! oh, love! oh,
mour! l'a - mour! L'a-mour est en - fant de Bo -
love! oh, love! A gyp - sy boy is Love, 'tis
p
16362

hême, Il n'a ja - mais, ja-mais con-nu de loi, Si tu ne m'ai-mes pas, je
true, He ev - er was and ev - er will be free; Love you not me, then I love
t'ai - me, Si je t'ai-me, prends garde à toi! Si tu ne
you, If I love you, be - ware of me! Love you not
f
pp
m'aimes pas, si tu ne m'aimes pas, je t'ai - me! Mais si je t'aime, si je
me, love you not me, then I love you! But if I love you, if I
cresc.
f
pp
cresc.
f
3
3
t'ai - me, prends garde à toi!
love you, be - ware of me!
mf
ff
Ped.

p
pp
L'oiseau que tu croy-ais sur-prendre, Bat-tit de l'aile et_s'en-vo-
As a bird, when you thought to net him, On buoyant wing escapes in
la; L'amour est loin, tu peux l'at-ten-dre; Tu ne l'at-tends plus, il est
air, Love is war-y when you a-wait him; A-wait him not, and he is
portamento
là! Tout au-tour de toi vi-te, vi-te, Il vient, s'en va,_puis il re-
there! All a-round you he swift-ly sweeps, Now here, now there he_ light-ly
portamento
vient; Tu crois le te-nir, il t'é-vi-te; Tu crois l'é-vi-ter, il te
flies; When you deem him yours, he es-capes; You'd fain es-cape, and you are

tient! L'a - mour! l'a -
his! Oh, love! oh,
mour! l'a - mour! l'a -
love! oh, love! oh,
p
mour! L'amour est en - fant de Bo - hême, Il n'a ja - mais, jamais con-nu de
love! A gyp - sy boy is Love, 'tis true, He ev - er was and ev - er will be
loi, Si tu ne m'ai - mes pas, je t'ai - me; Si
free; Love you not me, then I love you, If

je t'ai - me, prends garde à toi!
I love you, be - ware of me!
Si tu ne
Love you not
f
pp
m'ai - mes pas, si tu ne m'ai - mes pas, je t'ai - me!
me, love you not me, then I love you;
f
cresc.
Mais si je t'ai - me, si je t'ai - me, prends garde à toi!
But if I love you, if I love you, be - ware of me!
f
3
pp
cresc.
f
ff

Près des remparts de Séville

Seguidilla

from "Carmen"

English version by
Dr. Theodore Baker

Georges Bizet
(1838 - 1875)

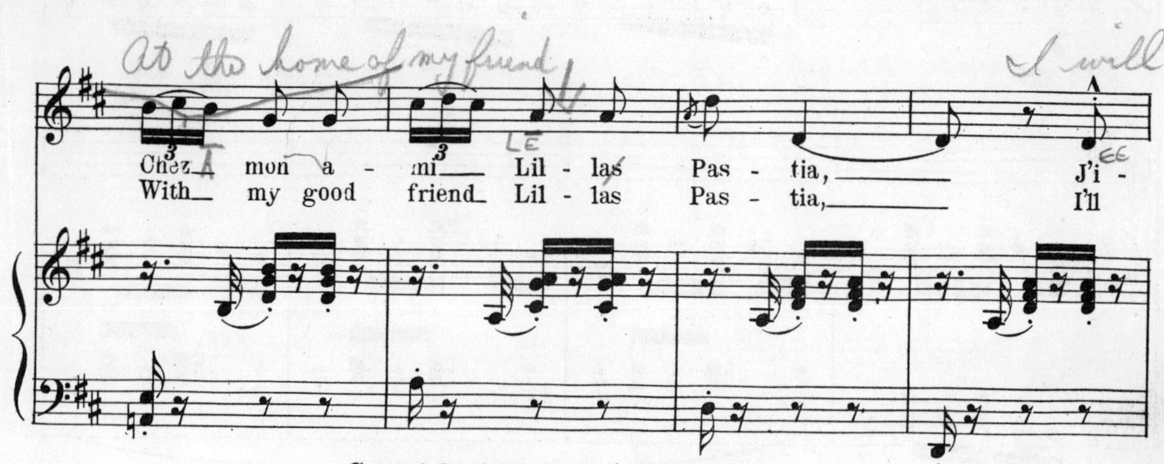

I'm going to dance the Seguedille and drink some Manzanilla.
rai dan - ser la Sé - gué - dille Et boi - re du Man - za -
soon dance the gay Se - gui - dil - la, And I'll drink Man - za -
nil - la.
nil - la.
I will go to the house of my friend
J'i - rai chez mon a - mi Lil - las
I'll go see my good friend Lillas
Pas - tia.
Pas - tia!
sempre pp

Yes, but all alone one is bored, and the true pleasures are for two,
sempre pp
Oui, mais tou-te seule on s'en-nui-e, Et les vrais plaisirs sont à deux;
But all a-lone what can one do? True joy be-gins when there are two;
Therefore, to keep me company, I will take my lover!
Donc, pour me te-nir com-pa-gnie, J'em-mè-ne-rai mon a-mou-reux!
And so, to keep me com-pa-ny, I'll take my lov-er dear with me!
My lover he is gone
p
Mon a-mou-reux il est au
My lov-er dear has got the
ten.
to the devil, I have put him to the door yesterday,
dia-ble, Je l'ai mis à la por-te hier!
mit-ten, And where he is, the deuce may care!

Mon— pau-vre coeur tres con-so-la-ble,
Now— my poor heart, so sad-ly smit-ten,
Mon— coeur est li-bre com-me l'air!
My— heart is free, is free— as air!
pp
J'ai des galants à la dou-zai-ne, Mais ils ne sont pas— à mon gré.
Though I have suitors by the dozen— There is not one that suits my whim;
rall.
Voi-ci la fin de la se-mai-ne: Qui veut m'ai-mer? je l'ai-me-
The week is gone, and none is chos-en: Who will love me? I will love
colla voce

a tempo
rai! Qui veut mon â - - me? Elle est à
him! Who'll have my soul? 'Tis for the
a tempo
pren-dre! Vous ar - ri - vez au bon mo -
ask - ing! Now some good fair - y has sent you
ment! Je n'ai guè - re le temps d'at - ten - dre, Car a - vec mon nou - vel a -
here! And my patience will bear no task - ing, For, be - side my new lov - er
mant, Près des rem - parts de Sé -
dear, Near to the walls of Se -
f
f

vil - le, Chez mon a - mi Lil - las Pas - tia,
vil - - la, With my good friend Lil - las Pas - tia,
Nous dan - se - rons la Sé - gué - dille Et boi - rons
We'll soon dance the gay Se - gui - dil - la, And we'll
du Man - za - nil - la. Tra la la la la la la la la la
drink Man - za - nil - la. Tra la la la la la la la la la
la, tra la la la la la la la la la la la.
la, Tra la la la la la la la la la la la.
sempre f
p
sf
ff

En vain pour éviter

Card Scene
from "Carmen"

English version by
Dr. Theodore Baker

Georges Bizet
(1838 - 1875)

La mort!
To die!
J'ai bien lu-
So it is.
moi d'a-bord,
First come I,
En-sui-te lui-
af-ter-wards he-
pour tous les deux,
Both of us are
la mort!
to die!
cresc.
Andante molto moderato ♩=66 with simplicity and very evenly
En vain pour é-vi-ter les ré-pon-ses a-
In vain, to shun the an-swer that we dread to

mè-res, En vain tu mê-le-ras, Ce-la ne sert a
hear, To mix the cards we try, 'Tis all of no a-
rien, les car-tes sont sin-cè-res Et ne men-ti-ront pas!
vail, they still re-main sin-cere, And they can nev-er lie!
Dans le li-vre d'en haut si ta page est heu-reuse, Mêle et cou-
If in the Book of Fate you have a shin-ing page, Se-rene-ly
poco sf
pe sans peur: La car-te sous tes doigts se tour-ne-ra joy-
cut and deal; The card that you shall turn will noth-ing ill pre-

pp
eu - se, T'an-non-çant le bon-heur!
sage, And fu-ture joy re-veal!
Mais si tu dois mou-
But if you are to
rir, Si le mot re-dou-ta-ble Est é-crit par le sort,
die, If that so dread-ful word Be writ by Fate on high,
poco cresc.
Re-com-men-ce vingt fois, la carte im-pi-to-ya-ble Ré-pé-te-
You may try twen-ty times, Un-pi-ti-ful the card Will but re-
ra: la mort!
peat: "You die!"
cresc. molto
Oui, si tu dois mou-rir, Re-com-men-ce vingt
Yes, if you are to die, You may try twen-ty
cresc.

ff
f
mf poco rit.
fois, la carte im-pi-to-ya-ble Ré-pé-te-ra: la
times, Un-pi-ti-ful the card Will but re-peat: "You
f dim. molto p dim. colla voce
a tempo
f
mort! En-cor!
die!" A-gain!
p
f
p
f
ff
En-cor! Tou-jours la
A-gain! All hope is
p
cresc.
f
ff
mort!
vain!
pp
f
p
8

Non più mesta

Cavatina

from "La Cenerentola"

English version by
Mrs. O. B. Boise

Gioacchino Rossini
(1792 - 1868)

pian- - -to, Sof- -frir ta- -cen- -do il
dow- - -er, Youth was spent in si- -lent
co- - - -re,
sor- - - -row,
col canto
pp
Ma per soa-ve in- - -can- - -to
Then dawned the mag-ic hour,
Del-l'e-tà mia nel fio- - -re,
My lone-ly days' bright mor- - -row,
cresc.

Co - me un ba - - le - - - - no
Forc - ing love's bud to
ra - pi - do, la sor - te mi - a, la sor - te mi - a can -
flow - er, Fill - ing with fra - grance my poor, emp - ty
giò, co - me un ba - le - - - - no
life, Forc - ing love's bud to
ra - - - - - - - pido, la sor - te mi - a, la sorte mia can-
flow - - - - - - - er, Filling with fragrance my poor, empty

Allegro
giò. No, no, no, no, ter-ge-te il
life. No, no, no, no, Ah, no more
ci-glio, perchè tre-mar, per-chè tre-mar, per-chè?
sighing, No, never-more shalt thou weep all a-lone.
A que-sto
Here on my
sen, a questo sen vo-la- - - - -te.
breast shall love for mourning a- - - - -tone.
Fi-glia, so-
Daugh-ter, and
f
p
rel- -la, a-mi-ca, tut-to, tutto, tut-to, tutto tro-
sis- -ter, and com-rade, alway, alway, alway, alway thou'lt
rallent.
3

vate in me, tro- -vate, tro-vate in
find them in me, thou shalt find them, find all in
a tempo
me.
me.
ff
a tempo
f
fz
fz
Meno
f
p
allegro
tr
tr
sf
p
Non più
Now fare-

grazioso
me-sta ac-can-to al fuo-co Sta-rò so-la a gor-gheg-giar! no! Ah, fu un
well, dark days of weeping! Love's warm sun hath dried my tears. Yes! Thrill'd with.
lam-po, un sogno, un gio-co Il mi-o lun-go pal-pi- - -
bliss be-yond all tell-ing, My full heart for- -gets its
tar! Non più me-sta ac-can-to al fuo-co, non più
fears. Yes, fare-well, then, dark days of weep-ing, Now fare-
me-sta ac-can-to al fuo-co Sta-rò so-la a gor-gheg-
well, long days of weep-ing! Love's warm sun hath dried my

giar! No! Ah, fu un lam - po, un so - gno, un gio - co Il mio
tears. Yes! Thrill'd with bliss be - yond all tell - ing, My
fz
p
lun-go pal-pi - tar! Non più
heart for - - gets its fears. Yes, fare-
me - sta ac - can - to al fuo - co, non più me - sta accan - to al
well, then, dark days of weep - ing! Thrill'd with bliss be - yond all
fuo - co Sta - rò so - la a gor - gheg - giar! Ah, fu un
tell - ing, My sad heart for - gets its fears, Thrill'd with

so - gno̮un lam - po̮un gio - co Il mio lun - go pal - pi -
bliss be - yond - all tell - ing, My glad heart for - gets - its
Più mosso brillante
tar, Ah, fu̮un lam - - - po, un so - gno̮un
fears! Thou, my loved one, hast come to
gio - - - - co, ah, fu̮un lam - po̮un so - gno̮un
save me, Fill - ing life with love and
gio - co̮Il mi - o lun - - go
joy un - told, with love and

pal- -pi- -tar, Ah, fu un lam- - - - -
joy un- -told, Thou, my loved
po, un so-gno un gio- - -co, ah, fu un
one, hast come to save me, Fill-ing
lam-po un so-gno un gio-co Il mi-o lun- - -go
life with love and joy un-told, with love and
pal- - -pi- -tar, Ah, fu un
joy un-told. Thrill'd with

gio - co, ah, fu un gio - co, ah, fu un lam - - - -
rap - ture past all tell - ing, Thrill'd with rap - ture past all
- - - - - - - - - po il pal - pi -
tell- - - - - - - - -ing, is my glad
tar, ah, fu un gio - co, ah, fu un gio - co, ah, fu un
heart, Thrill'd with rap - ture past all tell - ing, Yes, with
lam - - - - - - - - po il pal - pi -
rap - ture past all tell- - - - -ing, my hap - py

tar, il mio lun - go pal - pi - tar, il mio
heart, filled with joy, for-gets its fears, my glad
lun - go pal - pi - tar, il pal - pi - tar, il pal - pi -
heart for-gets its fears, yes, my glad heart for - gets its
tar, il pal - pi - tar!
fears, for-gets its fears!

Parto, parto

Aria
from "La Clemenza di Tito"

English version by
Lorraine Noel Finley

Wolfgang Amadeus Mozart
(1756 - 1791)

rò qual più ti piace, quel che vorrai fa-
all I will o-bey you; What you de-mand, I'll
fp
rò, vorrai farò.
be, I will a-gree.
f
ff
p
Par-to, ma tu, ben mi-o!
Dear-est, though I am leav-ing,
6
me-co ri-tor-na in pa-ce, sa-rò qual più ti
Loved one, come back, Oh, I pray you; In all I will o-

pia - ce,
bey you,
quel che vor - rai fa - rò, sì, sa -
What you de - mand, I'll be, Yes, com -
rò qual più ti pia - ce,
mand, and I'll o - bey you;
quel che vor -
What you de -
rai fa - rò,
mand, I'll be,
quel che vor - rai fa -
To all I will a -
rò, quel che vor - rai fa - rò.
gree, To all I will a - gree.

Allegro
Guar - da-mi e tut - to ob-bli - o, e a
Ven-geance you cry, while griev-ing, I
ven - di - car - ti io vo - lo, e a ven - di - car - ti io
fly, so do not chide me, I fly, so do not
vo - lo. Di quel - lo sguar-do
chide me; With your fair glance to
p dol.

so - lo
guide me,
io_ mi ri-cor-de-rò, io
I_ fol-low your de-cree; To
mi ri-cor - de-rò.
all I_ will a-gree.
Par - to!
Dear-est,
ma tu, ben mi-o! me-co ri-tor-na in pa-ce; sa-rò_ qual
though I am leav-ing, Come back with me, I pray you; In all_ I
fp
più_ ti pia-ce,_ quel che vor-rai fa-rò,
will_ o-bey you;_ What you de-mand, I'll be,

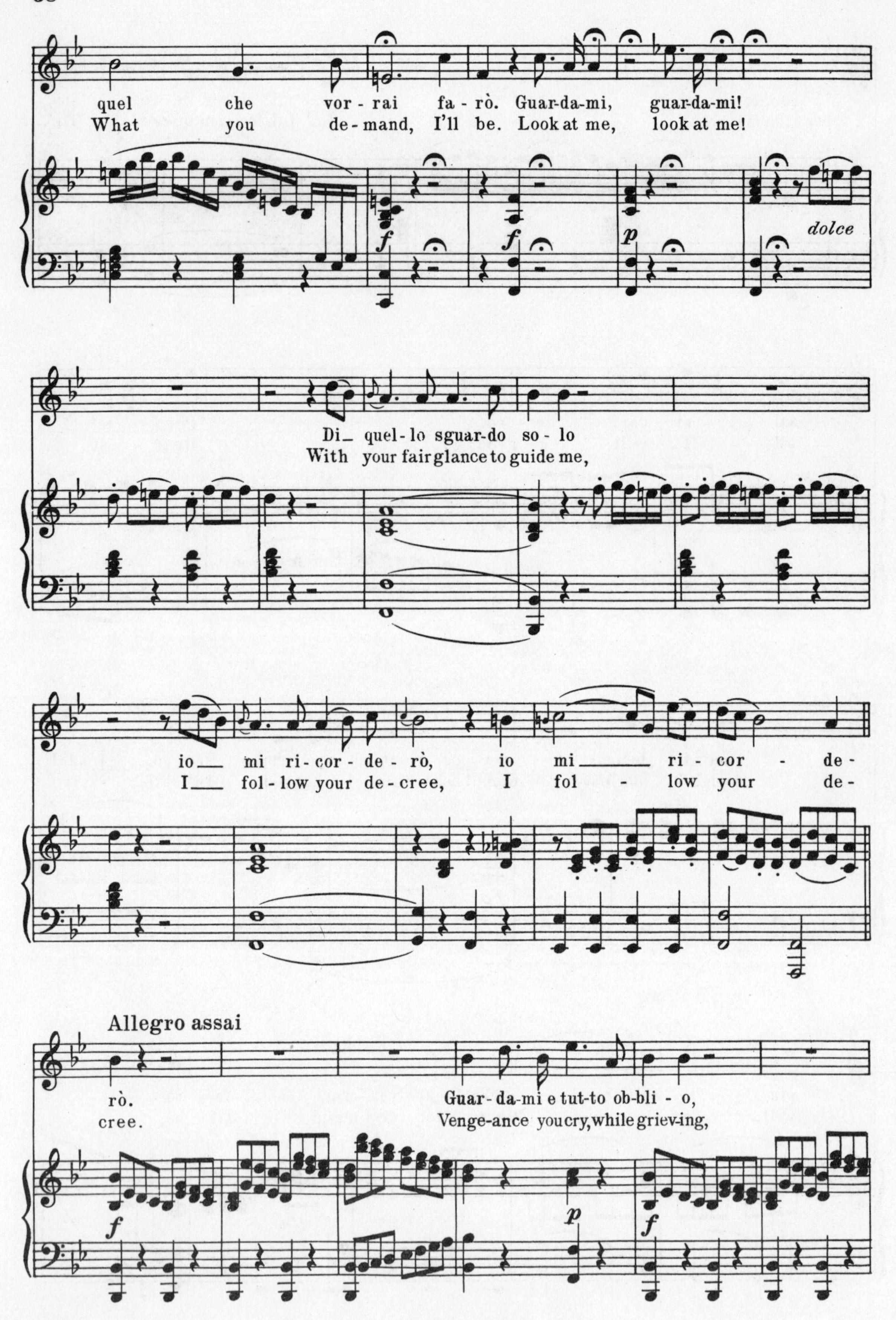
quel che vor-rai fa-rò. Guar-da-mi, guar-da-mi!
What you de-mand, I'll be. Look at me, look at me!
dolce
Di_ quel-lo sguar-do so-lo
With your fair glance to guide me,
io_ mi ri-cor-de-rò, io mi_ ri-cor-de-
I_ fol-low your de-cree, I fol-low your de-
Allegro assai
rò.
cree.
Guar-da-mi e tut-to ob-bli-o,
Venge-ance you cry, while griev-ing,

o a ven-di-car-ti io vo - lo.
Ah! dear-est, do not chide me.
Ah, qual po - ter, oh De - i! do-
Gods, O what pow'r you grant - ed, Be-
p
na - ste al-la bel - tà, do - na - ste al-la bel-
stow-ing beau-ty's charm, Be - stow - ing beau - ty's
tà, al-
charm! O
tr
la bel - tà, do - na
Gods, what pow'r, Be - stow
f
p

- - - ste al - la bel - tà, do - na - ste al-
- - - ing beau - ty's charm, Be - stow - ing
la bel - tà,
beau - ty's charm!
al - la bel - tà, ah, qual po-
O Gods, what pow'r, O Gods, what
f
p
ter, oh De - i! do - na - ste al - la bel - ty's
pow'r you grant - ed, Be - stow - ing beau - ty's

tà, do na - - - - - ste al - la
charm! What pow'r, O Gods,
fp
tr
bel - tà, al - la bel - tà, al -
what pow'r, What pow'r, O Gods, what
f
p
la bel - tà, al - la bel -
pow'r, Be - stow - ing beau - ty's
cresc.
tà!
charm!
f

Non più di fiori

Recitative and Aria

from "La Clemenza di Tito"

English version by
Dr. Theodore Baker

Wolfgang Amadeus Mozart
(1756 - 1791)

più del-la vi-ta su-a? che per tua col-pa di-ven-ne re-o?
more than for life he car-eth? for thy mis-do-ing be-came a trai-tor?
che t'ub-bi-di, cru-de-le? che, ingiusta, t'a-do-ra? che in faccia a morte si gran
Who in thy rage o-beyed thee, a-dored thee when un-kind! Who still is faithful, though by
fe-de ti ser-ba? e tu frat-tan-to, non i-gno-ta a te stes-sa,
death he be threatened? And yet thou go-est, well a-ware thou art guilt-y,
an-drai tranquil-la al ta-la-mo d'Au-gusto? Ah! mi ve-dre-
to meet Au-gus-tus and cel-e-brate thy bri-dal! Ah! all a-round

i sempre Se-sto d'in-tor-no! E l'au-re e i sassi te-merei che lo-qua-ci
me I shall see on-ly Sextus, The breezes, the rocks, I shall fear, will be tell-tales
p
mi scopris-se-rò a Ti-to.
to be-tray me to Ti-tus!
f
A' pie-di suo-i va-da-si il tutto a pa-lesar,
Before his feet I'll fall to admit my fault in full;
Si sce-mi il de-lit-to di Se-sto, se scu-sar non si può
Though Sex-tus be not quite un-of-fend-ing, I can light-en his blame
p

col fal-lo mi-o. D'im-per o e d'I-me-ne-i spe-ran-ze, ad-di-o!
by my en-deav-or. Ye hopes of love and pow-er, fare-well, then, for-ev-er!
Larghetto
p
dolce
Non più di fio - ri
No more en - tranc - ing
vaghe ca - te - ne di-scen-da I - me - ne ad in - trec -
gar-lands of flow - ers Hy-men de - scend - ing for me shall

cresc.
ciar. Stret-ta fra bar-ba-re, a-spre ri-tor-te,
twine, Fet-tered by bar-bar-ous, un-yield-ing pow-ers,
veg-go la mor-te ver me a-van-zar, veg-go la
Death I be-hold as he nears me ma-lign! Death I be-
mor-te ver me a-van-zar! Non più di fio-ri
hold as he nears me ma-lign! No more en-chant-ing
dolce
p
va-ghe ca-te-ne di-scen-da I-me-ne
gar-lands of flow-ers Hy-men de-scend-ing

ad in - trec - ciar, non più di fio - ri
for me shall twine, No more en-chant-ing
ad in - trec -
for me shall
va - ghe ca - te - ne di-scen-da I - me - ne ad in - trec -
gar - lands of flow - ers Hy-men de - scend - ing for me shall
Allegro
mf un poco agitato
ciar. In - fe - li - ce!
twine! Hap - less vic - tim!
mf
f
qual or - ro - re!
Doomed to lan - guish!
f

Ah, di me che si di -
Ah! how long, in dark - - est
p
f
p
rà? che si di - rà?
night! in dark - est night!
f
p espress.
espress.
Chi ve - des - se il mio do - lo - re, pur a -
Could one heart that knows my an - guish Fail to
vria di me pie - tà!
mourn my woe - ful plight?
chi ve - des - se
Could one heart
il mio do - lo - re,
that knows my an - guish
3
3

pur___ a - vria di me_ pie - tà,
Fail___ to mourn my woe - ful plight?
3
3
pur_ a - vria di_ me_ pie -
fail_ to mourn my_ woe - ful
tà!
plight?
con anima
Non più di fio - ri
No more en - chant - ing

va - ghe ca - te - ne di-scen - da I - me - ne
gar - lands of flow - ers Hy-men de - scend - ing
ad in - trec - ciar. Stret - ta fra
for me shall twine, Fet - tered by
bar - ba-re, a - spre ri - tor - te,
bar - bar-ous, un - yield - ing pow - ers,
veg - go la mor - te ver me a - van -
Death I be - hold, near - ing ma -

zar, veg - go la mor - te
lign, Death I be - hold, he
ver me a - van - zar! In - - fe -
nears me ma - lign! Hap - - less
li - ce! qual or - ro - re! Ah, di
vic - tim! Doomed to lan-guish! Ah! how
cresc.
f
me che si di - rà?
long, in dark - est night!
dolce
cresc.
f
p

dolce
Chi_ ve - des-se il mio_ do -
Could one heart that knows my
lo - re, pur a - vria di_ me pie - tà,
an-guish Fail to_ mourn my_ woe-ful plight?
chi_ ve-
Could one
des-se il mio_do - lo-re, pur_ a-vria di me_ pie -
heart that knows my_ an-guish Fail_ to mourn my woe-ful
tà,_ pur a - vria di_ me pie - tà!
plight? fail to mourn my woe - ful plight?

mf
cresc.
In - - - fe - li - ce! qual or -
Hap - - - less vic - tim! Doomed to
cresc.
f
dolce
ro - - re! Chi ve - des - se il mio do - lo - re, pur a -
lan - - guish! Could one heart that knows my an - guish Fail to
f
p
vria di me pie - tà! In - - fe - li - ce!
mourn my woe - ful plight? Hap - less vic - tim!
un poco agitato
qual or - ro - re! Non più di fio - ri vaghe ca - te - ne discenda I -
Doomed to languish! No more en - chanting garlands of flowers Hymen de -

cresc. poco a poco
me-ne ad in-trec-ciar. Stret-ta fra bar-ba-re, a-spre ri-
scend-ing for me shall twine, Fet-tered by bar-barous, un-yield-ing
fp fp fp fp
tor-te, veg-go la mor-te ver me a-van-zar!
pow-ers, Death I be-hold, he nears me ma-lign!
f
fp fp
cresc.
p
dolce
Chi_ ve-
Could one
des-se il mio do-lo-re,_ pur a-vria di_ me pie-tà, chi ve-
heart that knows my an-guish Fail to mourn my woe-ful plight? Could one

des - se il mio do - lo - re, pur a - vria di me pie - tà,
heart that knows my an - guish Fail to mourn my woe - ful plight,
cresc.
pie - tà, di me pie - tà,
to mourn my woe - - ful plight,
f
mf
cresc.
pie - tà, di me pie - tà,
to mourn my woe - - ful plight,
f
di me, di me
to mourn my woe - - -

tr
pie - - tà, pur a - vria di me - pie -
ful plight? fail to mourn my woe - ful
cresc.
cresc. molto
tà, pur a - vria di me - pie - tà, a -
plight? fail to mourn my woe - ful plight, to
fp fp
vria di me pie - tà!
mourn my woe - - - - ful plight?
fp fp
f

When I am Laid in Earth

Dido's Lament
from "Dido and Aeneas"

Nahum Tate

Henry Purcell
Edited by Ernst Victor Wolff

Air
mf
When I am laid, am
laid in earth, May my wrongs cre - ate No trou - ble, no
trou-ble in thy breast;
p
When I am laid, am
laid in earth, May my wrongs cre - ate No trou - ble, no

p
mf
trou-ble in thy breast: Re-mem-ber me, re-mem-ber me;
p
mf
f
but ah!_ for - get___ my fate. Re-mem-ber me, but ah!___
f
mf
for-get my_ fate.
mf
f
mf
p

O don fatale

Aria

from "Don Carlo"

Giuseppe Verdi
(1813 - 1901)

te - re, ti ma - le - di - co, ti ma - le - di - - co, o mia bel -
haughty, My curse is on thee! Yea, curs - es for my beauty
f
Più mosso
tà! Ver - sar, ver - sar sol pos - so il pian - to, Spe - me non
bright! With bit - ter tears my heart is riv - en, Hope nev - er
p
ho, sof - frir do - vrò! Il mio de - lit - to è orri - bil
comes in sor - row's night! My crime so great, though my life be
tan - to, Che can - cel - lar mai nol po - trò. Ti ma - le -
giv - en, To can - cel that no torture might. My curse is
f

di - co, ti ma-le-di - co, o mia bel - tà! Ah! ti ma-le-
on thee, my curse is on thee, O beauty bright! Ah! my curse is
f
di - co, o mia bel - tà!
on thee, O beau-ty bright!
ff
Andante ♩= 84 cantabile
O mia re-
O Queen a-
p
p
gi - na, io t'im - mo - la - i Al fol - le er
dor - ed, I sac - ri - ficed thee, O fool - ish
f

pp
3
ror di que-sto cor! So-lo in un
er-ror of this lov-ing heart! In some lone
p
f
3
chio-stro al mon-do o-ma-i Po-trò ce-
con-vent where none can find me, I can con-
ff
pp
lar il mio do-lor. Ohi-mè! ohi-
ceal my wild de-spair. A-las! a-
mè! O mia re-gi-na, so-lo in un
las! O Queen a-dor-ed, In some lone

string.
chio - stro al mon-do o - ma - i Po - trò ce - lar
con - vent where none can find me, I can con - ceal
string. col canto
cresc.
largamente
il mio do - lo - re; Ah! so-lo in un chiostro al mon-do o -
my wild de - spair; Ah! in some lone convent where none can
cresc.
mai Po - trò ce - lar il mio do - lor!
find me, I can con - ceal my wild de - spair!
Allegro agitato ♩ = 152
f
Oh ciel! e
Oh, heav'n! and
f

Car-lo... a morte do-ma-ni... gran
Car-lo... condemned to-mor-row... great
p
Dio,... for-se an-drà!
heav'ns! he may be!
cresc.
f
Ah! un dì mi re-sta, la spe-me m'ar-
Ah! one day is left me, 'Tis hope sweet-ly
col canto
f
lunga
con slancio
ri-de! Sia be-ne-det-to il
dawn-ing! Ah! thanks to heav'n be
col canto
f

ciel,__ be-ne-det-to il ciel!__ Lo__ sal-ve-rò! Un dì__ mi
giv'n,__ thanks to heav'n be giv'n,__ I'll save him yet! One day__ is__
re-sta, un dì__ mi re-sta, ah si - - a__ bene-det-to il
left me, one day__ is__ left me, Ah! thanks to__ heav'n, yes, thanks to__
cresc.
ciel,
heav'n,
lo__ sal-ve-rò!
I'll__ save him now!

Khivria's Song and Hopak

from "The Fair of Sorochinsk"

Transliteration by
Anna Heifetz
English version by
Lorraine Noel Finley

Modest Mussorgsky
(1839 - 1881)

*oo

Poco accelerando
poco a poco cresc.
f
Э, чтоб те-бе го - рил - ка в глот - ке пек-лом ста-ла,
*E, chtob te-*be go - ril - ka v glot - ke* pek-lom sta-la,
Oh, may the liq-uor burn your throat like rag-ing hell-fire,
cresc.
sf
а на за - кус - ку чор - то-вым хво - стом бы по-перх - нуть-ся,
a na za - kus - ku chor - to-vym khvo - stom by po-perkh - nut' - sya,
And may the food you eat be-come the Dev-il's tail and choke you,
cresc.
sf
a tempo
mf
да и за - ка-five-ться! Уж луч-ше бы ты с Хив-ри при-
da i za - ka-yat'-sya! **Uzh luch-she oy ty s Khiv-ri pri-
And may it gag your tongue! You ought to fol-low Khiv-ria's ex-
p
p
Più tranquillo
мер, то, взял: бе-реж - ли-вень-ка, да скром-нень - ка.
mer, to, vzyal: be-rezh - li-ven'-ka, da skrom-nen - ka.
am-ple more: She's de - mure and shy, she is thrift - y.
pp

* as in bet ** oo

* as in bet ** as in bit *** oo

че - рез го - ры,_ сер - день - ко, на ба - зар, на ба - зар.
che - rez go - ry,_ ser - den'- ko, na ba - zar, na ba - zar.
Car - ry - ing my_ bas - ket on mar - ket day, mar - ket day.
Тор - го - ва - ла буб - лы - ки ка - за - кам, ка - за - кам,
Tor - go - va - la bub - ly - ki ka - za - kam, ka - za - kam,
There the Cos - sacks bought_ all my gin - ger - bread, gin - ger - bread,
poco rallent.
втор - го - ва - ла буб - лы - ки в пя - та - ка, в пя - та - ка.
vtor - go - va - la bub - ly - ki v pya - ta - ka, v pya - ta - ka.
Mine was ex - tra good_ bak - ing, so they said, so they said.
poco rallent.
Andantino
ritard.
Нет, нет, не ви - дать; не при - дёт.
Net, net, ne ni - dat'; ne pri - diot.
No, no, he'll not come, I'm a - fraid.
ritard.
p
dim.

Poco più mosso. Agitato
Уж не за друго ли бес погнал тебя, проклятый.
*Uzh ne za dru-goi li bes po-gnal te-bya, pro-klya-tyi.
You are run-ning af-ter some-one else, a-las! The Dev-il
Так узнаешь ты про Хиврю: ой, накажет больно, скажешь, что довольно.
Tak uz-ma-yesh ty pro Khiv-ryu: oi, na-ka-zhet bol'-no, ska-zhesh,chto do-vol'-no.
catch you, curs-ed one, But Khiv-ria soon will scold you round-ly, Box your ears quite sound-ly.
risoluto
Agitato
Да, ну их к бесу в пекло!
Da, nu ikh k be-su v pek-lo!
The Dev-il take the scoun-drel!
Più tranquillo
Полно, Хивря, не журися;
Pol-no, Khiv-rya, ne zhu-ri-sya;
Why this flur-ry? Stop your wor-ry.
commodo assai
rallent.
веселенька будь, песенку спевай Ах!
ve-se-len'-ka bud', pe-sen-ku spe-vai. Akh!
Khiv-ria, sing a song, sing a care-free song, Ah!

*oo

Allegretto scherzoso
От ко-ли-ж я Бру-дэ-у-са встре-ти-ла, встре-ти-ла,
Ot koli-zh ya Bru-de-u-sa vstre-ti-la, vstre-ti-la,
Since I read his first en-tranc-ing bil-lets-doux, bil-lets-doux,
не од-ни же че-ре-ви-ки зно-си-ла. зно-си-ла,
ne od-ni zhe che-re-vi-ki zno-si-la, zno-si-la.
I have worn out, gai-ly danc-ing, man-y shoes, man-y shoes.
Цур, то-би, Бру-дэ-у-су! Пэк, то-би, Бру-дэ-у-су!
Tzur, to-bi, Bru-de-u-su! Pek, to-bi, Bru-de-u-su!
Oh, may the Dev-il shake you! Oh, may old Sa-tan take you!
Са-ма со-би ди-ву-ю-ся, с Бру-дэ-у-сом це-лу-ю-ся,
Sa-ma so-bi di-vu-yu-sya, s Bru-de-u-som tze-lu-yu-sya,
Won-der at my fol-ly fills me when this bump-kin comes and thrills me,

poco rallent.
са - ма со - би ди - ву - ю - ся, с Бру - дэ - у - сом це - лу - ю - ся!
sa - ma so - bi di - vu - yu - sya, s Bru - de - u - som tze - lu - yu - sya!
Won - der at my fol - ly fills me when this bump-kin comes and thrills me!
poco rallent.
a tempo
mf
На Бру - дэ - у - се ча - пан,
Na Bru - de - u - se cha - pan,
Peo - ple dress as best they can;
a tempo
mf
dim.
p
что твой пан, что твой пан!
chto tvoĭ pan, hto tvoĭ pan!
spic and span is my man!
*У Бру - дэ - у - са чо - бо - ты
*U Bru - de - u - sa cho - bo - ty
He's a pea-cock full of dar - ing,
толь - ко выш - ли из ра - бо - ты. Цур, то - би, Бру - дэ - у - су!
tol' - ko vysh - li iz ra - bo - ty. Tzur, to - bi, Bru - de - u su!
so I meek - ly go on car - ing. Oh, may the Dev - il break you!
f
sf
sf
* oo

Пэк, то-би, Бру-дэ-у-су! Са-ма со-би ди-ву-ю-ся,
Pek, to-bi, Bru-de-u-su! Sa-ma so-bi di-vu-yu-sya,
Oh, may old Sa-tan take you! How ab-surd to be e-lat-ed
sf
sf
p
Бру-дэ-у-сом лю-бу-ю-ся, са-ма со-би ди-ву-ю-ся,
Bru-de-u-som lyu-bu-yu-sya, sa-ma so-bi di-vu-yu-sya,
ev-'ry time for him I've wait-ed, How ab-surd to be e-lat-ed
poco rallent.
a tempo, ma allargando
Бру-дэ-у-сом лю-бу-ю-ся!
Bru-de-u-som lyu-bu-yu-sya!
ev-'ry time for him I've wait-ed!
poco rallent.
a tempo, ma allargando
mf sf
sf
mf
Бру-дэ-ус ли-хой ка-зак,— лю-бит мак, лю-бит мак,
Bru-de-us li-khoi ka-zak,— lyu-bit mak, lyu-bit mak,
He's a Cos-sack, big and strong, likes to sleep all day long;
p sf
sfp
sfp
sfp

Любит на пе - чи ва - лять - ся, толь - коб к ве - че - ру под - нять - ся.
Lyu - bit na pe - chi va - lyat - sya, tol' - kob kve - che - ru pod - nyat - sya.
Pop - py seeds have made him la - zy. Such a loaf - er drives me cra - zy.
sfp
f
Ну, то - би, Бру - дэ - у - су! Где - ж, то - би, Бру - дэ - у - су!
No, to - bi, Bru - de - u - su! Gdezh, to - bi, Bru - de - u - su!
Oh, may the Dev - il wake you! Oh, may old Sa - tan take you!
Са - ма со - би ди - ву - ю - ся, с Бру - дэ - у - сом ми - лу - ю - ся!
Sa - ma so - bi di - vu - yu - sya, s Bru - de - u - som mi - lu - yu - sya!
How could I have made this blun - der? Why am I in love, I won - der?
poco rallent.
Са - ма со - би ди - ву - ю - ся, с Бру - дэ - у - сом ми - лу - ю - ся!
Sa - ma so - bi di - vu - yu - sya, s Bru - de - u - som mi - lu - yu - sya!
How could I have made this blun - der? Why am I in love, I won - der?
poco rallent.

Energico
f
Бру - дэ - у - са на вой - ну, —
Bru - de - u - sa na voi - nu, —
Were a bat - tle cry to sound, —
f
p
а Бру - дэ - ус: "не пой - ду, мне ми - лей в мо - ги - лу ле - чи,
a Bru - de - us: "ne* poi - du, mne* mi - leĭ v mo - gi - lu le - chi,
he'd pre - fer a grass - y mound, Hid - den deep from can - non - ad - ing,
mf
лишь бы не слы - хать кар - те - чи." Чтож э - то Бру - дэ - у - су?
lish by ne sly - khat' kar - te - chi." Chtozh *e - to Bru - de - u - su?
rath - er than with troops pa - rad - ing. Oh, may the Dev - il shake you!
f
fsf
sf
sf
Как же э - то, Бру - дэ - у - су? Са - ма со - би ди - во - ва - лась,
Kak zhe e - to, Bru - de - u - su? Sa - ma so - bi di - vo - va - las',
Oh, and may old Sa - tan take you! Cow - ard - ice and fear a - larm me;
sf
sf
sf
p

* as in bet

с Бру-дэ-у-са стос-ко-ва-лась; са-ма со-би ди-во-ва-лась,
s Bru-de-u-sa stos-ko-va-las; sa-ma so-bi di-vo-va-las',
nev-er-more his smile can charm me. Cow-ard-ice and fear a-larm me;
poco rallent.
с Бру-де-у-са стос-ко-ва-лась. А как под ве
s Bru-de-u-sa stos-ko-va-las', A kak pod ve-
nev-er-more his smile can charm me. Af-ter dark an-
Meno mosso
mf
poco rallent.
pp
чер в ма-ли-не шеп-чет Бру-дэ-ус див-чи-не:
cher v ma-li-ne shep-chet Bru-de-us div-che-ne:
oth-er meets him where the wood-land path is lone-ly,
"Ты, див-чи-на, не чу-рай-ся. Бру-дэ-у-сом ве-ли-чай-ся!"
"Ty, div-chi-na, ne chu-rai-sya, Bru-de-u-som ve-li-chaĭ-sya!"
She a-dores him, she en-treats him, "Love me on-ly, love me on-ly!"

f
Цур, то-би, Бру-дэ-у-су! Пэк, то-би, Бру-дэ-у-су!
Tzur, to-bi, Bru-de-u-su! Pək, to-bi, Bru-de-u-su!
Oh, may the Dev-il break you! Oh, may old Sa-tan take you!
fsf
sf
Tempo I
Тут у-же не ди-во-ва-лась, с Бру-дэ-у-сом рас-кви-та-лась!
Tut u-zhe ne di-vo-va-las', s Bru-də-u-som ras-kvi-ta-las'!
His neg-lect is my vex-a-tion. Now I'm done with all flir-ta-tion!
p
poco rallent.
Тут у-же не ди-во-ва-лась, с Бру-дэ-у-сом рас-кви-та-лась!
Tut u-zhe ne di-vo-va-las', s Bru-də-u-som ras-kvi-ta-las'!
His neg-lect is my vex-a-tion. Now I'm done with all flir-ta-tion!
Andantino
Ах! Рас-кви-та-лась! О ой!
Akh! Ras-kvi-ta-las! O-oi!
Ah! all flir-ta-tion! O-ho!
psf

Faites - lui mes aveux

Aria
from "Faust"

English version by
H. T. Chorley and Dr. Theodore Baker

Charles Gounod
(1818 - 1893)

Allegro agitato ♩. = 88

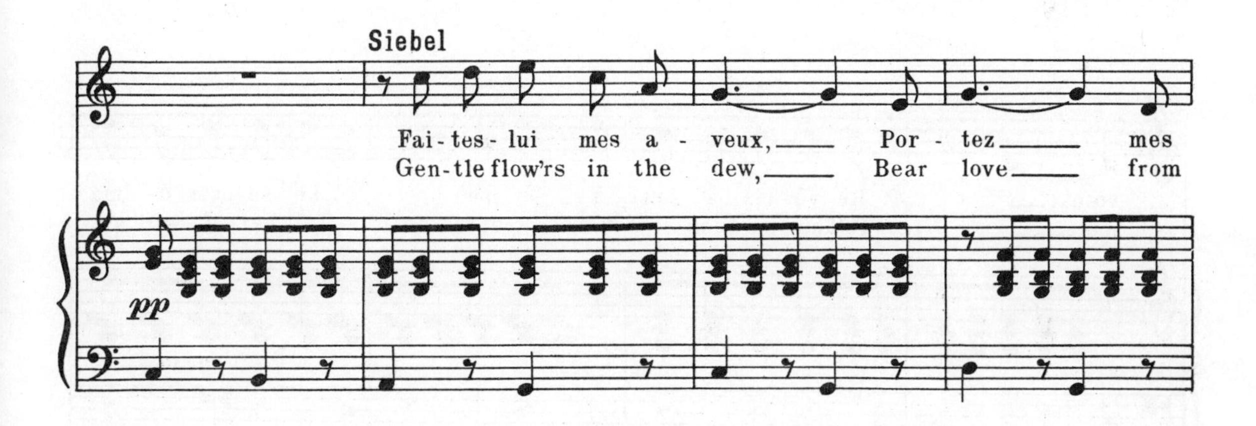

bel - le, Que mon coeur nuit et jour Lan - guit d'a -
fair - er, Dear-er to me than all, Though fair you
cresc.
mour! Fai-tes-lui mes a - veux, Por - tez mes
be! Gen-tle flow'rs in the dew, Bear sighs from
pp
voeux! Ré-vé-lez à son â - me Le se-cret de ma
me! Tell my pas-sion so ten - der, Tell her I will de -
cresc.
flam - me, Qu'il s'ex-hale a-vec vous Par-fums plus
fend her, E'en my life will sur - ren - der, Her knight to
dim.

doux!
be!
p
cresc.
Andante
Recit.
Fa-né - e! hé-las! ce sor-cier, que Dieu dam-ne, M'a por-té mal-
'Tis with - ered! A-las! That dark stran-ger fore-told me what my fate must
f
Tempo I
heur!
be!
p
cresc.
Andante
Recit.
Je ne puis, sans qu'el-le se fa - ne, Tou-cher u-ne
Nev-er to touch a sin-gle flow - er, but it must de-
fp

fleur! Si je trem-pais mes doigts dans l'eau bé-ni-te!
cay! Sup-pose I dip my hand in ho-ly wa-ter!
p
pp
Andante ♩=56
C'est là que cha-que soir vient pri-er Mar-gue-ri-te! Voy-
'Tis here, when day is o'er, that she prays! Mar-gue-ri-te! Yes,
p
Allegro
ons main-te-nant! voy-ons vi-te! El-les se fa-nent?...
now I will try! and this mo-ment! Can it be with-ered?
p
p
pp molto cresc.
Tempo I. Allegretto
non!... Sa-tan, je ris de toi! C'est en vous que j'ai
No! Thou fiend! thy pow'r is gone! Gen-tle flow-ers, lie
f
dim.

foi; Par-lez pour moi! Qu'el-le puis-se con-naî-tre
there, And speak for me: Say how wea-ry my wait-ing,
p
L'é-moi qu'el-le fait naî-tre, Et dont mon cœur trou-blé N'a
How my heart is beat-ing, While to Her in the air I
cresc.
point par-lé! C'est en vous que j'ai foi! Par-lez pour
bend my knee. Gen-tle flow-ers, lie there And speak for
pp
moi! Si l'a-mour l'ef-fa-rou-che, Que la fleur sur sa
me! If my love should a-larm her, May the flow-ers to
cresc.

bou - che Sache au moins dé - po - ser Un doux bai-
charm her Meet her lip to re - lease A ten - der
dim.
ser! Un bai - ser, un doux bai-
kiss! To re - lease a ten - der
espress.
p
ser! Un bai - ser, un doux bai - ser!
kiss, to re - lease a ten - der kiss!
rit.
a tempo
colla voce
f a tempo

O mio Fernando

Recitative and Cavatina
from "La Favorita"

Gaetano Donizetti
(1797 - 1848)

lento
Tut - to mel di - ce... e dub - bia l'al - ma an - co - ra all' i - nat -
Scarce dare I say it; my doubt - ing sens - es fal - ter with un - ex -
lento
te - sa gio - ja. Oh Di - o! spo - sar - lo...
pect - ed rapture. Ye pow - ers! to wed him!
oh mia ver - go - gna e - stre - ma... in do - te al prode re - car il di - so -
O how I shrink with hor - ror! Bring him in dowry a - lone the stain of
Allegro
nor! no... ma - i do - ves - si e - se - crar - mi... fug - gir! saprà in brev'
shame! No! e - ven al - though he may curse me, I fly, ere love im -
o - ra chi sia la don - na che co - tan - to a - do - ra.
plores him To pit - y aught the out - cast who a - dores him.
f

Andante cantabile
p
p
p espress.
O mio Fer-
O my Fer-
nan-do! del-la ter-ra il tro-no A pos-se-der-ti a-
nan-do! Earth's enchantments of plea-sure, Lav-ished with-out thee, en-
vrai do-na-to il cor;
trance my heart no more;
Ma pu-ro l'a-mor mi-o
Ho-ly and pure af-fec-tion

co-me il per-do - no, Dan - na-to, a-hì las-sa! e a di-spe-ra-to or-
dims like heaven's a - zure When smi-ling se - ren - est, dark clouds roll be -
ror...
fore.
Il ver fia no - - to,
The truth be spo - - ken,
leggiero ma tranquillo
e in tuo di-spre-gio e-stre - mo La pe - na a -
truth that will scathe and shame me; The doom, though
vrom - mi che maggior si de'!...ah!
fear - ful, I de-serve it all! Ah!
rall.
col canto

a tempo
p
Se il giu-sto tuo di - sde - gno al - lor, al-lor— fia sce - mo,
Just-ly his in - dig - na - tion a - lone, a - lone will blame me,
p
Piom - bi, gran Di - o, piom - bi, gran Di - o, la fol-gor tua su
Cause,—God of Ven - geance, cause, God of— Vengeance, on me thy bolt to
colla voce
me! Ah, se fia sce-mo il tuo di - sde - gno, piombi, o Dio, la fol-gor tua su
fall, His in-dig-na - tion then will blame me, God of Ven-geance, cause thy bolt to
me! Ah, se fia scemo il tuo di - sde - gno, piom-bi, o Di - o, la fol-gor tua su
fall. His in-dig-na-tion then will blame me; God of Vengeance, on me thy bolt will
Quasi Recit.
f
me! Su, cru - de - li... e chi v'ar-
fall! Ye tor - mentors, why spare mine
colla parte f

110

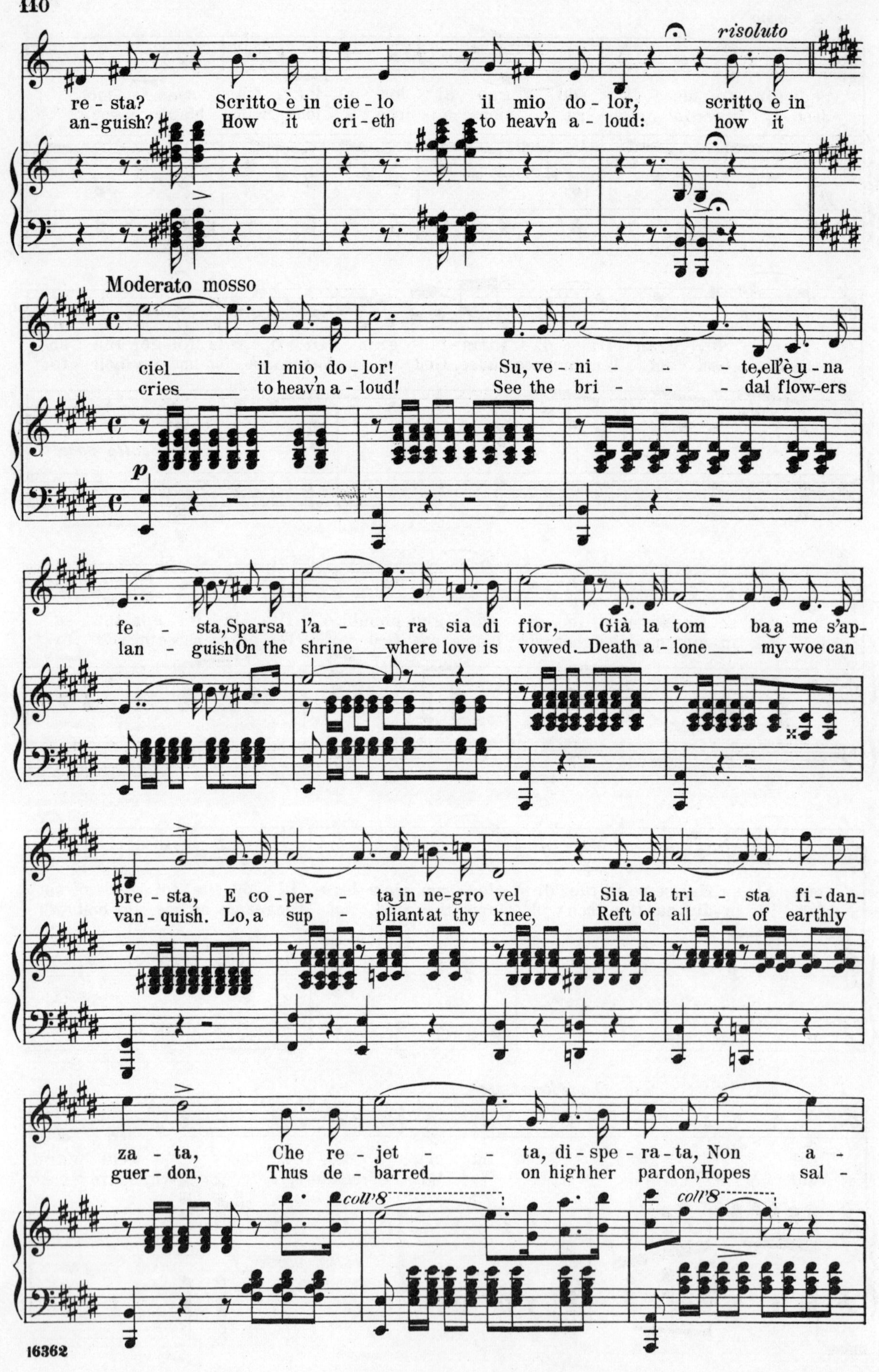
risoluto
re - sta? Scritto è in cie - lo il mio do - lor, scritto è in
an - guish? How it cri - eth to heav'n a - loud: how it
Moderato mosso
p
ciel il mio do - lor! Su, ve - ni - te, ell'è u - na
cries to heav'n a - loud! See the bri - dal flow - ers
fe - sta, Sparsa l'a - ra sia di fior, Già la tom ba a me s'ap -
lan - guish On the shrine where love is vowed. Death a - lone my woe can
pre - sta, E co - per - ta in ne - gro vel Sia la tri - sta fi - dan -
van - quish. Lo, a sup - pliant at thy knee, Reft of all of earthly
za - ta, Che re - jet - ta, di - spe - ra - ta, Non a -
guer - don, Thus de - barred on high her pardon, Hopes sal -
coll'8
coll'8
16362

vrà perdo - no in ciel... male-det - ta, di-spe-ra -
va - tion yet in thee, Thus debarred heav'n-ly par -
ta, non a-vrà per-do-no in ciel, no, non a - vrà, ma-le-det -
don, Hopes sal-va-tion yet in thee, Thus, thus de - barred heav'nly par -
cresc.
ta, di-spe-ra - ta, non avrà perdo-no in ciel, non avra perdo-no in
don, heav'nly par - don, Hopes salva-tion yet in thee, hopes salva-tion yet in
cresc.
f
Allegro
ciel... ah! non a - vrà per-do - no in ciel!
thee, ah! hopes sal - va-tion yet in thee!
f
p
f
f
Ah, cru-de - li, e
Ye tor - men - tors,

16362

chi var - re - sta? Scrit - - to in cie - - lo è il
see mine an - guish! How it cries to
f
mio do - lor, scrit - to in cie - - lo è il
heav'n a - loud, how it cries to
mio, do - lor!
heav'n a - loud!
f
Cru - de - li, ve - ni - te!...
Tor - men - tors, tor - men - tors!

Tempo I
Scritto è in ciel il mio dolor... Su, ve-ni - te, ell'è u-na
How it cries to heav'n aloud! See, the bri - dal flowers
fe - sta, Spar-sa l'a - ra sia di fior, Già la
lan - guish On the shrine where love is vowed: Death a-
tom - ba a me s'ap-pre - sta, E co-per - ta in ne-gro
lone my woe can van-quish. Lo! a sup - pliant at thy
vel Sia la tri - sta fi-dan-za-ta, Che re-
knee, Reft of all of earth-ly guer-don, Thus de-
jet - ta, di-spe-ra-ta, Non a-vrà perdo - no in
barred on high her pardon, Hopes sal - va - tion yet in
p
cresc.
f

ciel, maledet - ta, di - spe-ra - ta, non a-vrà per-dono in
thee, Thus de-barred heav'n-ly par - don, Hopes sal-va-tion yet in
ciel, no, non a - vrà, ma-le-det - ta, di - spe-ra - -
thee, hopes sal-va - tion yet, Thus de-barred heav'n-ly par - -
cresc.
ta, non a-vrà per-do-no in ciel, non a-vrà per-do-no in
don, Hopes sal-va-tion yet in thee, hopes sal-va-tion yet in
cresc.
cresc.
f
ciel... ah! non a - vrà per-do - no in ciel... Ah! la
thee, ah! hopes sal - va-tion yet in thee! Ah! de-
f
p
tri - - sta fi - dan-za - - - ta Non a-
barred heav'n-ly par - - don, Hopes sal-

vrà, non a - vrà per - don - no in
va - tion, sal - va - tion yet in
ciel... ah! non a - vrà per - do - - no in
thee, ah! hopes sal - va - - tion yet in
ciel... ah! non a - vrà per - do - - no in ciel!...
thee, ah! hopes sal - va - tion yet in thee!
Ma - le - det - ta, di - spe - ra - ta, non a - vrà per - do - no in
Thus debarred on high her par - don, Hopes sal - va - tion yet in
ciel!
thee!

Chacun à son goût

Prince Orlofsky's Song
from "Die Fledermaus"

English version by
Ruth and Thomas Martin

Johann Strauss
(1825-1899)

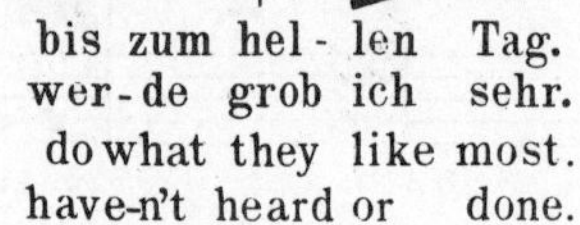

poco meno
spricht; in-dess, was mir als Wirt steht frei, duld ich bei Gä-sten nicht. Und
spruch; nicht lei-den kann ich's, wenn sie schrein: ich will nicht, hab ge-nug! Wer
wit, But what as host I am al-lowed in guests I won't per-mit! If
ford, But I have nev-er found a way to keep from be-ing bored. I
poco meno
marcato
se-he ich, es en-nü-yiert sich je-mand hier bei mir, so pack ich ihn ganz
mir beim Trin-ken nicht pa-riert, sich zie-ret wie ein Tropf, dem wer-fe ich ganz
I find an-y-one chez moi who's bored or is a bore, I pick him up and
do not care for mu-sic much, not e-ven Jo-hann Strauss. The op-er-et-ta
p marcato
un-ge-niert, werf ihn hin-aus zur Tür, so pack ich ihn ganz un-ge-niert, werf
un-ge-niert die Fla-sche an den Kopf, dem wer-fe ich ganz un-ge-niert die
un, deux, trois, I toss him out the door! I pick him up and un, deux, trois, I
I hate most is called "Die Fle-der-maus," The op-er-et-ta I hate most is
f
f

16362

ihn hin-aus zur Tür. Und fra - gen Sie, ich bit - te, war-um ich das denn
Fla - sche an den Kopf. Und fra - gen Sie, ich bit - te, war-um ich das denn
toss him out the door! My guests en - joy their free-dom in an - y - thing they
called "Die Fle-der - maus." There's noth - ing you could men-tion that I would care to
pp
poco rit.
a tempo
tu, war-um ich das denn tu? 's ist mal bei mir so Sit-te, cha-cun à son goût! 's ist
tu, war-um ich das denn tu? 's ist mal bei mir so Sit-te, cha-cun à son goût! 's ist
do, in an - y - thing they do. We Rus-sians have a cus-tom: Cha-cun à son goût! We
do, that I would care to do. It is Or - lof-sky's cus-tom: Cha-cun à son goût! It
a tempo
poco rit.
cresc.
1.
2.
mal bei mir so Sit-te, cha-cun à son goût!
mal bei mir so Sit-te, cha-cun à son goût!
Rus-sians have a cus-tom: Cha-cun à son goût!
is Or - lof-sky's cus-tom: Cha-cun à son goût!
cresc.
f
f
f

Voce di donna

The Blind Girl's Song

from "La Gioconda"

English version by
F.W. Rosier

Romance.

Amilcare Ponchielli
(1834 - 1886)

allarg.
te - ne - bre di quel - la _ san - ta, di quel - la santa il vol - to.
void of _ sight, Can see _ thy _ fea - tures, can see _ thy fea - tures nev - er.
col canto
morendo
affrett.
Pu - re da me non par - ta - si, da me non
Yet I would of - fer, ere we part, A to - ken
a tempo
p
affrett.
rall.
par - ta - si, senza un pie - to - so don, no! no! A
from my heart, from my sad, grate - ful heart! Ah! Ah! This
col canto
a tempo
te que - sto ro - sa - rio che le pre - ghie - re a -
ro - sa - ry I give thee, Round it my heart - felt
pp leggerissime

du - na, Io te lo por-go, ac - cet - ta - lo, ti par - te -
prayers cling, Deign to ac-cept the gift from me, It will good
rà for - tu - na. Sul - la tua te - sta
for - tune to thee bring: And on thy head for -
p
espandendosi
vi - gi - li la mia be - ne - di - zion, sul - la tua
ev - er near Shall be my heart - felt prayer! shall be my
pp
allarg. molto
a tempo
te - sta, sul - la tua te - sta vi - gi - li la
prayer, shall be my heart - felt prayer, shall be my
ff allarg. molto
a tempo

mi - a be - ne - di - zion,
heart-felt, my heart - felt prayer,
pp
pp a tempo
la mia be - ne - di - zion vi - gi - li, vi - gi -
shall be my heart-felt prayer, ev - er near, ev - er
pp
li, ah! sul - la tua te - sta vi - gi - li la mi - a
near, Ah! shall be my heart-felt prayer, shall be my prayer,
be - ne - di - zion.
shall be my prayer!
pp

Stella del marinar

Scena and Romanza

from "La Gioconda"

English adaptation by
Henry Hersee

Amilcare Ponchielli
(1834 - 1886)

Ah! u - na Ma-don - na!
Ah! 'tis a Ma-don - na!
pp agitato
Andantino agitato
con passione
Stel - la del ma - ri - nar!
Star of the mar - i - ner!
pp
Ver - gi - ne San - ta, tu mi di - fen - di in que-st'o-ra su-
Vir - gin most ho - ly, Be my de - fen - der in this hour of
pre - ma, tu ve - di quan-ta pas - sio - ne e quan-ta
tri - al! Thou see - est by how much ar - dor, by how much
pp

fe de mi tras - se a ta - le au - da - cia es - tre - -
faith I am led to ad - ven - ture this au - da - cious
ma! Sot - to il tuo ve - lo
step! Un - der thy man - tle,
che i pro - stra - ti am - man - ta ri - co - ve - ra co -
kneel ing sin - ners shelt - 'ring, Find ref - uge for
ste - i che pre - ga, e tre - ma. Ah!
one who is pray - ing and trem - bling. Ah!

Meno
dolciss.
Scen - da per que - sta fer - vi - da o - ra -
Send down in an - swer to my fer - vent
pp
zio - ne sul ca - po mi - o, Ma -
prayer Up - on my head, O
pp
string.
don - na del per - do - no, scen - da sul ca - po
Vir - gin, full of mer - cy, Up - on my head send
col canto
mio u - na be - ne - di - zion, sul ca - po
down a bless-ing from on high, Up - on my
cresc.

mio, sul ca - po mi - o u - na be - ne - di -
head send down, O Vir - gin, A bless-ing from on
Più accelerato
cresc. agitato
zion. O Ver - gin, su me di-
high! O Vir - gin, thy bless - ing from on
p
cresc. agitato
lunga a piacere
scen - da la tua be - ne - di - zio - ne,
high, Be - stow on me a bless - ing,
f
col canto
rall. molto
Largo
la tua be - ne - di - zion, la tua be - ne - di - zion.
Be - stow on me a bless - ing, a bless - ing from on high!
col canto pp

Höre mit Sinn

Waltraute's Narrative
from "Die Götterdämmerung"

English version by
Frederick Jameson

Richard Wagner
(1813 - 1883)

rit-ten wir ängst-lich zu Heer; Wal - hall's mu - thi-ge Hel - den mied
wil-dered we rode to the field; Val - hall's he - roes no more may meet
cresc.
mf dim.
pp
sf p
Wal - va - ter. Ein - sam zu Ross, oh-ne Ruh' noch
War - fa - ther. Lone - ly to horse, with-out pause or
(tenuto)
Rast, durch-streift' er als Wand' - rer die Welt.
rest, as Wand' - rer he swept through the world.
cresc.
Jüngst kehr te er heim; in der Hand
Home came he at last; in his hand
mf dim.
dim.
pp
cresc.

hielt_ er sei-nes Spee - res Split-ter, die hat-te ein
hold - ing the spear - shaft's splin-ters: a he-ro had
dim.
p
dim.
Held ihm ge-schla-gen.
struck it a-sun-der.
Mit stum - men
With si - lent
pp
pp
Wink Wal-hall's Ed-le wies er zum Forst, die
sign Val-hall's he-roes sent he to hew the
cresc.
Welt - E-sche zu fäl-len.
world-ash-tree in piec-es.
ten.
mf
ten.
dim.
p
dim.
più p

Etwas breit, doch nicht schleppend
Des Stam-mes Schei - te hiess er sie schich-ten zu ra-gen-dem
The sa-cred stem at his command was riv - en and raised in a
pp
marcato
p
Hauf rings um der Se li-gen Saal. Der Göt-ter Rath liess er be-ru-fen;
heap round a-bout the hall of the blest. The ho-ly host called the to-geth-er;
molto tenuto
den Hoch - sitz nahm hei - lig er ein: ihm zu Sei-ten
the god on his throne took his place. In dis-may and
hiess er die Ban - gen sich set - zen, in Ring und Reih' die
fear at his word they as-sem - bled; a-round him ranged the
cresc.
Ped.

Hall' er - fül - len die Hel - den.
hall was filled by his he - roes.
poco f
dim.
p
sempre dim.
etwas zurückhaltend
più p
pp
Ped.
Mässig
So sitzt er, sagt kein Wort,
So sits he, speaks no word,
pp
auf heh - rem Sit - ze stumm und ernst; des Spee - res Split - ter fest in der
on high en - thron - ed grave and mute; the shat - tered spear - shaft fast in his

Faust;
grasp;
Hol-da's Äp-fel
Hol-da's ap-ples
rührt er nicht an.
tastes he no more.
rallent.
sempre pp
Noch langsamer
Stau - nen und Ban - gen
Awe - struck and shrink-ing
bin - den starr die Göt - ter.
sit the gods in si - lence.
pp zögernd
pp
Etwas weniger gedehnt
Sei - ne
Forth on
pp zögernd
pp
pp
Ra - ben bei - de
quest from Val - hall
sandt' er auf
sent he his
Rei - se;
ra - vens;
kehr - ten die
if with good

einst mit gu - ter Kun - de zu - rück, dann noch
ti - dings back the mes - sen-gers come, then for -
ein mal - zum letz - ten Mal! - lä - chel-te
ev er shall smiles of joy glad - den the
pp dolce
e wig der Gott.
face of the god.
più p
pp
Wieder bewegt, wie vorher
Sei - ne Knie' um-win - dend lie - gen wir Wal - kür - en; blind
Round his knees en-twin - ing cow - er we Val - ky - ries; nought
sf
p
pp

bleibt er den fle - hen-den Bli-cken: uns al-le ver-zehrt Za - genundend-lo-se
recks he nor knows of our an-guish: we all are con-sumed by ter-ror and ne'er-end-ing
Angst. An sei-ne Brust presst' ich mich wei-nend;
fear. Up-on his breast weep-ing I pressed me;
sf
p
pp
rall.
zögernd
da brach sich sein Blick; er ge-dach-te, Brünn-hil-de, dein!
then soft grew his look; he re-mem-bered, Brünn-hil-de, thee!
p
Tief seufzt' er auf, — schloss das Au-ge, und wie im
He closed his eyes, — deep-ly sigh-ing, and as in
più p

Trau - me raunt' er das Wort: "des tie - fen Rhei - nes
slum - ber spoke he the words: if e'er the riv - er
pp
pp
Töch - tern gä - be den Ring sie wie - der zu - rück,
maid - ens win from her hand a - gain the ring,
3
p
Ped.
von des Flu - ches Last er - lös't wär'
from the curs - e's load re - leased were
dolcissimo
Langsam
Gott und Welt!"
god and world!
pp
ppp

Adieu, forêts

Recitative and Aria

from "Jeanne d'Arc"

English version by
Dr. Theodore Baker

Peter Ilyitch Tchaikovsky
(1840 - 1893)

Allegro moderato
Pourquoi, mon cœur, pour-quoi bats-tu si fort? Pour-quoi fré-mir? L'ef-froi rem-plit mon â - me!
But whence this fear I feel within my heart? Why fails my soul, and wherefore doth it trem - ble?
espress.
cresc.
p marcato
Andantino (Alla breve)
Adieu, fo-rêts, a-dieu, prés fleuris,
Farewell, ye mountains, ye be-lov-ed

champs d'or, Et vous, pai - si - bles val - lons, a - dieu!
mead - ows! Ye smil - ing val - leys, fare ye well for aye!
p
poco cresc.
Jeanne au - jour - d'hui vous dit à ja - mais, à ja - mais a - dieu.
No long - er now a - mong ye I may wan - der, to all to - day
più f
rit.
f
poco più mosso
Oui, pour tou - jours, tou - jours, a - dieu!
I bid a long fare - well! Fare - well!
p
mf
Mes prés fleu - ris et mes fo - rêts om -
Ye mead - ows all, ye shad - ow - haunt - ed

cresc.
3
breu-ses,
for-ests,
Vous fleu - ri-rez pour d'au-tres que pour
Ah, when I am gone, ye still so fair will
poco cresc.
moi.
be!
f
A-dieu, fo-rêts, eau
Ah, fare ye well, ye
mf
pu - re de la sour-ce: Je vais par-tir et ne vous
caves and cool-ing foun-tains! For Joan de-parts, and nev-er-
riten.
ver - rai plus, Jean-ne vous fuit, et pour ja -
more shall see ye, for Joan de - parts, and nev - er -
f
col canto

riten.
mais, oui, pour ja - mais.
more shall see ye.
dim.
riten.
Tempo I
p
O doux val - lon où j'ai con - nu la
To all the joys that we have known to -
p
poco cresc.
joi - e! Au - jour-d'hui je te quit - te, doux val -
geth - er I bid fare - well to - day for - ev - - er -
dim.
lon! Et mes a - gneaux, dans
more; And ye, my lambs, dis -
cresc.
p
poco cresc.

les ver - tes prai - ri - - es de - man - de - ront en
perse o'er yon - der heath - - er: No shep - herd have ye
Più mosso
vain leur gui - le!
now to go be - fore!
cresc.
mf
Au champ d'hon - neur je dois gui -
For I for - sake this flock to
poco a poco
der les bra - ves,
tend an - oth - er
cresc.
cueil - lir les pal - mes san -
On far - off, gor - y

ff
glan - - tes de la vic - toi - re! Je
fields, the fields of war! The
molto cresc.
(♩=♩)
vais où les voix m'ap-pel - - lent, Voix
Lord's command Himself on me im-pos - - eth, No
ff
sain - - tes, voix saintes qui m'ap-pel - - lent! Sei-
vain desire my willing heart en - clos - - eth: Ma-
Ped.
gneur, vous voy-ez au fond de mon â - me!
don - na! Thou know-est all my as-pi-ra - tion!
f
16362
Ped.
Ped.

riten.
dim.
Mon cœur se bri - se, Mon â - me souf - fre, Mon cœur se bri -
Thou see'st my trem - bling, and all my sor - row, thou see'st my trem -
riten.
dim.
p
Tempo I
- se, mon cœur sai - gne! O monts ai - més, a - dieu, a -
- bling and my sor - row. For - ev - er - more fare - well, ye
p
dieu, fo - rêts ombreu - ses, Et vous, pai - si - bles val -
moun - tains all and meadows, ye smil - ing val - leys, fare ye
lons, a - dieu! Jean - ne au - jour - d'hui vous
well for aye! No long - er now a -
3
p

cresc.
dit — à ja - mais, à ja - mais a - dieu! Oui,
mong ye I may wan - der, to all to - day I
cresc.
f
Più mosso
f
pour tou - jours, tou - jours, a - dieu. Prés fleu-
bid a long fare - well! Fare - well! Ye
f col canto
p
cresc.
ris, — ar - bres verts, Si chers à mon en - fan - ce,
meadows all a - round, ye shad - ow - haunt - ed for - ests,
Vous fleu - ri - rez pour d'au - tres que pour moi. A-
when I am gone, ye still so fair will be! Fare-
mf
p
cresc.

dieu, mes champs, a-dieu, val-lon, sour-ce pu-re, Il
well, then, fare ye well, ye caves and cool-ing foun-tains, for
mf
cresc.
faut par-tir, il faut par-tir et pour tou-jours! Ah! re-ce-
I de-part, for I de-part, for I de-part, and nev-er,
cresc.
ff a piacere
ff
vez mon é-ter-nel a-dieu!
nev-er-more shall see ye!
Tempo I
ff
p
Cor.
dim.
pp

Entweihte Götter!

Ortrud's Curse
from "Lohengrin"

English version by
Natalia Macfarren

Richard Wagner
(1813 - 1883)

Ra - che!
ven - geance!
Be - straft
De - clare
Ped.
ff
die
your
Schmach,
pow'r,
die
be
fp
hier
nigh
euch an - ge - than!
in this dread hour!
Stärkt mich im Dienst eu rer
Strike them with death who pro-
pp

heil' - gen Sa - che! Ver - nich - tet der
fane your al - tars! And strength - en my
f
ff
p
Ped.
Ab - trünn' - gen schnö den Wahn!
soul to a - venge your wrongs!
fp
molto cresc.
ff
Ped.
ff
Wo - dan!
O - din!
Dich Star ken
Thou strong and
p
ru - fe ich!
might - y one!
Frei - a!
Frey - a!
ff
p
Ped.

Er - hab' - ne, hö - re mich! Seg - net mir
Oh, Queen, bend down to me! Pros - per my
p
p
Trug und Heu-che-lei, dass glück - lich mei-ne
cause with dead-ly guile, Im - mor - tals, on my
ffp
cresc.
Ra - - - che sei!
ven - - - geance smile!
ff
ff
8
8

Connais-tu le pays

Romance

from "Mignon"

English version by
Dr. Theodore Baker

Ambroise Thomas
(1811 - 1896)

dim.
pp
— et des ro - ses ver - meil - les, Où la bri - se est plus douce
— lights the leaf - y gloom? Where the breeze soft - ly sighs,
pp
— et l'oi-seau plus lé - ger, — Où dans tou-te sai - son — bu-
— and the winds gent-ly lave — Si - lent myr - tle - trees, — and
sempre dolce
ti - nent les a - beil - les, Où ray-on-ne et sou - rit, comme un bienfait de
high the lau-rels wave, Where so ra-diant-ly calm, like blessing from on
pp
poco cresc.
dim.
Dieu, Un é - ter - nel prin - temps sous un ciel tou - jours bleu?
high, Smiles an e - ter - nal spring, ev - er blue is the sky
8
dim.

p
Hé - las! que ne puis - je te sui - vre Vers ce ri - vage heu-
Ah, me! where-fore may I not wan - der un - to that hap - py
pp
reux d'où le sort m'e - xi - la! C'est là, c'est là que je vou - drais
shore? Fain with thee I would fare! 'Tis there! 'Tis there, in love ev - er
p
f
mf
vi - vre, Ai - mer, ai - mer et mou - rir! C'est là que je vou - drais
fond - er, I fain would live and die! 'Tis there, in love ev - er
dim.
Tempo I
vi - vre, c'est là! oui, c'est là!
fond - er, I'd live, I would die!
Ped.
ritenuto

pp
sf
dim.
p
Andante
Con - nais - tu la mai - son où l'on m'at - tend là - bas? La
Hast thou e'er seen the house? In its pil - lared walls, They
pp
sal - le aux lam - bris d'or, où des hom - mes de mar - bre
stand wait - ing for me! How re - splen - dent the halls!
pp
M'ap - pel - lent dans la nuit en me ten - dant les
And mar - ble sculp - tures there seem to call out to
pp
Ped.
Ped.
Ped.

bras, Et la cour où l'on danse à l'om-bre d'un grand
me: "Hap-less maid-en, re-turn! Thy home is here for
Ped.
ar-bre, Et le lac trans-pa-rent, où glis-sent sur les
thee!" And the clear, shin-ing lake whereon there glides a-
p
pp
poco cresc.
dim.
eaux Mil-le ba-teaux lé-gers pa-reils à des oi-seaux?
long Man-y a sway-ing boat with danc-ing and with song!
dimin.
Hé-las! que ne puis-je te sui-vre Vers ce pa-ys loin-
Ah me! wherefore may I not wan-der un-to that hap-py
p
pp

tain d'où le sort m'e-xi - la! C'est là, c'est
shore? Fain with thee I would fare! 'Tis there, 'Tis
là que je voudrais vi - vre, Ai-mer, ai-mer et mou - rir! C'est
there, in love ev-er fond - er, I fain would live and die, 'Tis
là que je voudrais vi - vre, c'est là! oui, c'est là!
there, in love ev-er fond - er, I'd live, I would die!
dim.

Me voici dans son boudoir

Gavotte

from "Mignon"

English version by
Dr. Theodore Baker

Ambroise Thomas
(1811 - 1896)

*The role of Frederick, the page, is traditionally sung by an alto.

Allegretto
te!
rooms?
Me voi-
Here am
ci dans son bou - doir Et je sens mon cœur, je sens mon cœur bat - tre dés -
I in her bou - doir, And I feel my heart, I feel my heart beat high with
poir! Ah! je guet - te l'in - stant de la — re -
hope! Ah! I wait — for the hour when we — shall
voir, —
meet. —
Oui, je sens mon
Yes, I feel my

cœur, je sens mon cœur bat-tre d'es - poir! Co - quet - te, je
heart, I feel my heart beat high with hope! Co - quette, here I
guet - te l'in - stant de te re - voir.
wait for the hour when we shall meet!
Il faut en - fin vain-cre la cru - el - le,
Ah, cru - el fair, in the end I'll van - quish.
Il faut tou - cher, tou - cher le cœur de l'in - fi -
She must be made, she must be made to heed my

cresc.
dè - le, il faut tou - cher le cœur de l'in - fi - dè - - -
an - guish! She must be made to heed, to heed my an - - -
cresc.
- - le! Je suis dans son bou - doir Et je sens mon
- - guish! I'm here in her bou - doir, And I feel my
p
dim.
p
cœur, je sens mon cœur bat - tre d'es - poir! Ah! je
heart, I feel my heart beat high with hope! Ah! I
tr
cresc.
tr
p
guet - te l'in - stant de la re - voir!
wait for the hour when we shall meet!
tr
p
f
f

Moi je veux qu'on m'ai - me et j'es -
I would have her love me, and I
p
pè - - - - re, oui, j'es-père à mon tour être heu -
hope, Ah, yes, I hope to en - joy, as I
cresc.
reux; tant pis, ma foi, pour tous ses a-mou - reux, tant pis pour tous ses a-mou -
woo. How sad 'twill be for all who love her too! How sad for all who love her
dim.
reux, tant pis, ma foi! Je suis dans son bou - doir, Et je sens mon
too, who love her too! I'm here in her bou - doir, and I feel my
8
p

cœur bat-tre d'es-poir, bat-tre d'es-poir! Ah! je
heart, I feel my heart beat high with hope! Ah, I
8
tr
guet - te l'in - stant de la re - voir!
wait for the hour when we shall meet!
tr
p
Ah! je sens mon cœur, je sens mon cœur bat-tre d'es-
Ah! I feel my heart, I feel my heart beat high with
8
p
poir! Co quet - te, je guet - te l'in-
hope! Co-quette, here I wait the hour, the
tr
tr
f
8
f
tr

rit.
p
stant de_te re - voir. Pour mon coeur quel doux es -
hour when we shall_ meet! For my heart, how dear the
a tempo
8
pp rit.
p
poir! Voi - ci l'in - stant, c'est l'in-stant de la re -
hope! 'Tis now the_ hour, 'tis the hour when we shall
mf
voir, Pour mon coeur quel doux es - poir, mon coeur bat, oui, mon coeur
meet! For my heart, how dear the hope! Yes, my heart beats high, beats
dim.
bat d'es - poir!
high with_ hope!
f
pp
ff

Non so più cosa son

Aria
from "Le Nozze di Figaro"

English version by
Ruth and Thomas Martin

Wolfgang Amadeus Mozart
(1756 - 1791)

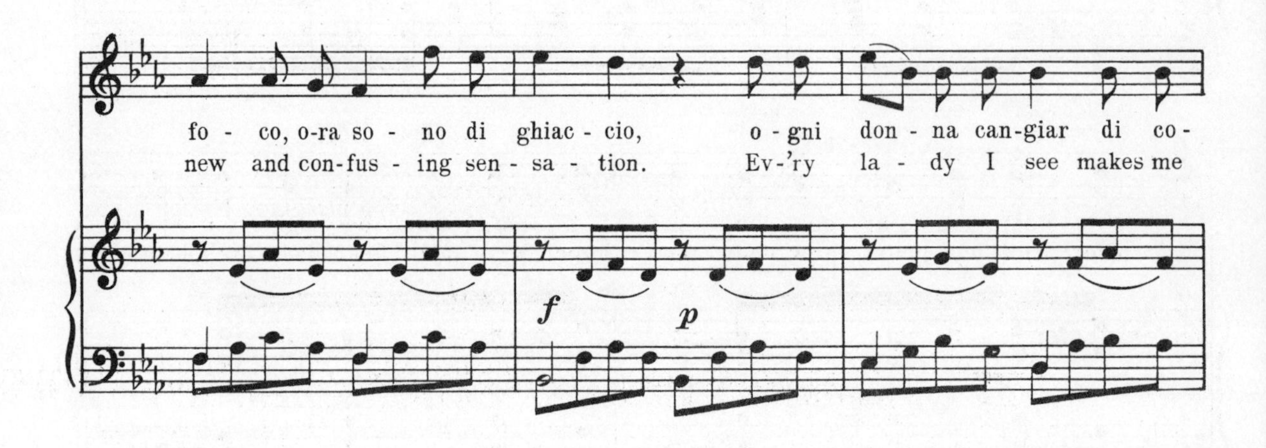

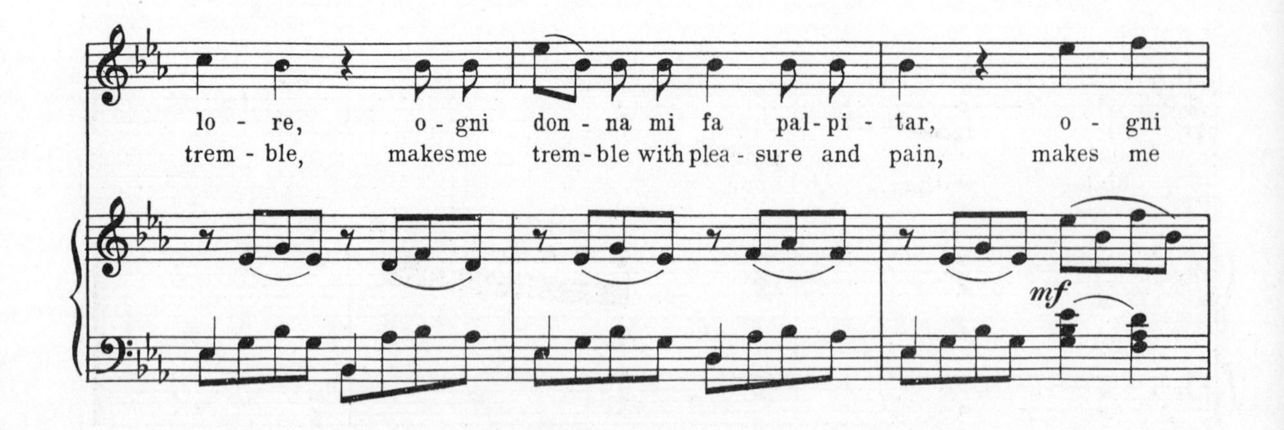

don-na mi fa pal-pi-tar, o-gni don-na mi
trem-ble with plea-sure and pain, makes me trem-ble with
p
p
mf
p
fa pal-pi-tar. So-lo ai no-mi d'a-mor, di di-
plea-sure and pain. When of love there is mere-ly a
p
cresc.
let-to, mi si tur-ba, mi s'al-te-ra il pet-to,
men-tion, I am spell-bound and rapt with at-ten-tion.
e a par-la-re mi sfor-za d'a-mo-re
I weave ro-manc-es and day-dreams to-geth-er,

un de - si - o, un de - si - o ch'io non
filled with long-ing, filled with long - ing I
pos - so spie - gar, un de - si - o, un de -
can - not ex - plain, filled with long - ing, filled with
si - o ch'io non pos - so spie - gar.
long - ing I can-not ex - plain.
Non so
If I
più co - sa son, co - sa fac - cio, or di fo - co, o - ra so - no di
knew what it is I'd con - fess it, but I am at a loss to ex -
f
p
p

ghiac - cio, o - gni don - na can-giar di co - lo - re, o - gni
press it, yet I know that it al - ways ex - cites me, that it
f
p
don - na mi fa pal - pi - tar, o - gni don - na mi
thrills me a - gain and a - gain, that it thrills me a -
mf
p
fa pal - pi - tar, o - gni don - na mi fa pal - pi -
gain and a - gain, that it thrills me a - gain and a -
mf
p
tar. Par - lo d'a-mor ve -
gain. Love is my in - spi -

glian - do,
ra - tion,
par - lo d'a - mor so -
on - ly con - sid - er -
gnan - do, all' ac - qua, all'om - bra, ai mon - ti, ai fio - ri, all'er - be, ai
a - tion. In riv - ers, woods, and flow - ers, I feel its mag - ic
fp
fon - ti, all' e - co, all' a - ria, ai ven - ti, che il suon de' va - ni ac -
stream - ing, a - wake, a - sleep, and dream - ing. In gen - tle winds and
fp
f
p
cen - ti, por - ta - no via con se, por - ta - no
show - ers, I hear its mel - low tone, I hear its
cresc.
f
colla voce
p

via con se. Par - lo d'a-mor ve - glian - do,
mel - low tone. Love is my con - ver - sa - tion,
par - lo d'a-mor so - gnan - do, all' ac - qua, all' om - bra,
theme with-out var - i - a - tion, I tell my love - song
ai mon - ti, ai fio - ri, all' er - be, ai fon - ti, all'
to glens and moun-tains, to riv - ers and foun-tains, to
e-co, all' a - ria, ai ven - ti, che il suon de' va - ni ac - cen - ti,
moon and stars in heav - en. The gen - tle breez - es ech - o
cresc.
f
p
cresc.

por - ta - no via con se,
my ev - 'ry word and tone,
por - ta - no via con
my ev - 'ry word and
f
colla voce
p
Adagio
se. E se non ho chi m'o - da, e
tone. And if no one will lis - ten... and
se non ho chi m'o - da,
if no one will lis - ten,
Tempo I
par - lo d'a - mor con
then I will talk a
cresc.
me, con me, par - lo d'a - mor con me.
lone of love, talk to my - self a - lone.
p
f

Voi, che sapete

Arietta

from "Le Nozze di Figaro"

English version by
Ruth and Thomas Martin

Wolfgang Amadeus Mozart
(1756 - 1791)

Andante con moto

p

Cherubino

Voi, che sa - pe - te che co - sa è a - mor,
You know the an - swer, you hold the_ key,

Don - ne, ve - de - te, s'io l'ho nel cor,
Love's ten - der se - cret— share it with me,

16362

Don - ne, ve - de - te, s'io l'ho nel cor.
La - dies, I beg you, share it with me.
Quel - lo ch'io pro - vo, vi ri - di - rò,
This new sen - sa - tion I un - der - go,
È per me nuo - vo ca - pir nol so.
It is so dif - f'rent from all I know.
Sen - to un af - fet - to pien di de - sir,
Filled with ex - cite - ment, walk - ing on air,

Ch'o - ra è di - let - to, ch'o - ra è mar - tir.
First I am hap - py, soon I de - spair.
Ge - lo, e poi sen - to l'al - ma av-vam - par,
Now I am chil - ly, next time a - flame,
E in un mo - men - to tor - no a ge - lar.
Not for a mo - ment am I the same.
Ri - cer - co un be - ne fuo - ri di me,
I am pur - su - ing some sun - ny ray,

Non so chi il tie - ne, non so cos' è. So-spi-ro e
But it e - ludes me, try as I may. I can't stop
ge - mo sen-za vo - ler, Pal - pi - to e tre - mo sen-za sa -
sigh - ing, hard as I try, And then I trem - ble, not know-ing
fp
per. Non tro-vo pa - ce not - te, nè dì, Ma pur mi pia - ce
why. From this di - lem-ma I find no peace, And yet I want it
mfp
lan - guir co - sì. Voi, che sa - pe - te
nev - er to cease. You know the an - swer,

che co - sa è a - mor, Don - ne, ve - de - te,
you hold the key, Love's ten - der se - cret,
s'io l'ho nel cor, Don - ne, ve - de - te,
share it with me, La - dies, I beg you,
s'io l'ho nel cor, Don - ne, ve - de - te,
share it with me, La - dies, I beg you,
s'io l'ho nel cor.
share it with me.
3
3
tr
tr

Che farò senza Euridice

Recitative and Aria

from "Orfeo"

Christoph Willibald von Gluck
(1714 - 1787)

chia-mo in-van! Mi-se - ro
call her in vain. Oh, what
me! la per-do e di nuo-vo e per sempre! oh leg-ge! oh mor-te! oh ri -
mis'ry to lose her a - gain and for-ev-er! O judgment, O sad death, cru-el
cor - do cru - del! Non ho soc - cor - so... non m'a - van - za con -
rec - ol - lection! I have no help - er, naught gives me con - so -
siglio... io veggo so-lo (Oh fie-ra vi-sta!) il lut-tu - o - so aspet-to del-
lation, naught can I image, (O fearful vision!) naught but the dark, gloomy aspect, the
l'or-ri-do mio sta-to! Sa - zia - ti, sor - te re - a... son di-spera - to!
horrors of my being! Now fate may wreak her vengeance, I am despairing.
f
16362

Allegretto
p
p
Che fa - rò senza Eu - ri - di - ce? Do-ve an-drò senza il mio
Live with - out my dear Eu - ri-di-ce! Can I live without my
ben? Che fa - rò? Do - ve an - drò? Che fa - rò sen - za il mio
love? In my woe, where can I go? Whith-er wan-der with no
f
f
ben? Do - ve an - drò sen - za il mio ben? Eu-ri-
love? whith-er wan-der with no love? Eu -

di - ce! Eu-ri - di - ce! oh Di - o! ri - spon-di...
ri-di-ce! Eu - ri-di-ce! O Heav-en! now tell me,
Adagio
ri - spon - - di... Io son pu - re il tuo fe -
Oh, tell me, I am for-ev-er thy true
p col canto
Tempo I
de - le, io son pu - re il tuo fe - del, il tu - o fe - de - le! Che fa -
lov - er, I am for - ev - er thy true lov - er, true lov - er! Live with-
rò senza Eu - ri - di - ce? Dove an-drò senza il mio ben? Che fa -
out my dear Eu - ri-di-ce! Could I live with-out my love? In my
f

rò?__ do - ve an - drò?__ che__ fa - rò__ sen - za il mio ben? Do - ve an-
woe, where can I go?__ Whith-er__ wan-der__ with no__ love, whith-er__
f
Moderato
drò__ sen - za il mio__ ben? Eu-ri - di - ce! Eu-ri - di - ce!
wan-der__ with no__ love? Eu - ri-di-ce! Eu - ri-di-ce!
Adagio
Ah! non m'a - van-za più__ soc-cor-so, più__ spe-ran-za nè dal
Through darkness groping, no__ help giv - en, Noth-ing hoping from earth or
Tempo I
mon - do. nè__ dal ciel! Che fa - rò senza Eu - ri -
heav - en. from earth or heav'n! Live with - out my dear Eu-

di - ce? Dove an - drò senza il mio ben? Che fa - rò? Do - ve an -
ri - di - ce! Whither wan - der with no love? In my woe, where can I
drò? Che fa - rò sen - za il mio ben? Do - ve an - drò? Che fa -
go? Whith - er wan - der with no love? Where can I go in my
rò? Do - ve an - drò sen - za il mio ben, sen - za il mio ben,
woe? Whith - er wan - der with no love, with - out my love,
sen - za il mio ben?
with - out my love?
f
f
f
f

Pauline's Aria

from "Pique Dame"

Transliteration by
Anna Heifetz
English version by
Rosa Newmarch

Peter Ilyitch Tchaikovsky
(1840 - 1893)

ру - ги_ ми - лы - я, въ без - печ - но - сти иг-
ru - gi_ mi - ly - ya, v bez - pech - no - sti ig-
friends for_ whom I sing, Who know nor care nor
ри - вой, подъ пля - со - вой на - пѣвъ вы рѣз - ви - тесь въ лу-
ri - voi, pod plya - so - voi na - pev vy rez vi - tes vlu
sor - row, But still can sport in hap - py groves and sun - ny
più f dim.
гахъ. Й я какъ вы жи - ла въ Ар-
gakh. I ya kak_ vy zhi - la v Ar-
fields, I too once dwelt a - mong the
p
ка - ді - и сча - стли - вой, и я на у - трѣ
ka - di - i shcha - stli - voi, i ya na *u - trye
peace - ful groves of Ar - ca - dy, Have hailed the dawn of
f
più f

* oo

дней въ сихъ ро-щахъ и по-ляхъ ми-ну-тны ра-до-сти вку-си-ла,
dneĭ v sikh roshchakh i po-lyakh mi-nu-tny ra-do-sti vku-si-la,
joy-ful days up-on this self-same earth, And known the bliss of liv-ing,
mf
ми-ну-тны ра-до-сти вку-си
mi-nu tny ra-do-sti vku-si
and known the bliss, the bliss of liv-
p
ла. Лю-бовь въ меч-тахъ зла-тыхъ мнѣ
la. Lyu-bov' v mech-takh zla-tykh mne
ing. The gold-en dreams of love, my
p
cresc.
сча-сті-е су-ли-ла, но чтожъ до-ста-лось мнѣ въ сихъ
scha-sti-ye su-li-la, no chtozh do-sta-los' mne v sikh
earl-ier years have bright-ened, A-las! of all those fair and
poco cresc.

ff
ра-дост-ныхъ мѣстахъ, въ сихъ ра-дост-ныхъ мѣстахъ, въ сихъ ра - дост-
ra-dost-nykh mes-takh, v sikh ra-dost-nykh mes-takh, v sikh ra - dost-
ra-diant vi-sions Now re-mains one hope a-lone, one hope re-
mf
ныхъ мѣс-тахъ: мо-ги ла, мо-ги ла, мо-
nykh mes-takh: mo-gi - la, mo-gi - la, mo-
mains a-lone: Death calls me, Death calls me, Death
dim.
ги - - ла!
gi - - la!
calls me!
p
p

Ah! mon fils!

Arioso

from "Le Prophète"

English version by
H. Millard

Giacomo Meyerbeer
(1791 - 1864)

dimin.
p
tha, que ton a - mour! Ah! mon fils, ah! mon
tha, who claimed thy heart! Ah! my son! Ah! my
smorz.
pp
p
fils, tu viens, hé - las! de don - ner pour ta mè - - re plus
son! For thou, a - las! thou dost give for thy moth - -er more
que la vie, en don - nant ton bon - heur, ton bon - heur!
than thy life, For thou giv'st all the joy of thy soul!
pp
p
f
Ah! mon fils, ah! mon fils, que vers le
Ah! my son! Ah! my son! now up to

ciel, que vers le ciel s'é - lè - ve ma pri -
heav'n, now up to heav'n my pray'r, my pray'r as -
è - re,
cends for thee;
et sois bé - ni
May heav-en's bless-ings
dans le Sei-gneur, mon fils, sois bé-ni, sois bé-ni, sois bé -
ev-er be with thee, my son, bless-ed be, bless-ed be, bless-ed
ni dans le Sei-gneur, sois bé
be, for-ev- -er-more, Bless thee
fpp
Ped.
dolce
molto cresc
f
p
col canto

Cadenza
f
ni, mon fils, mon fils, sois bé - ni dans le Sei-
now, my son, my son, May heav'n's choic - est blessing
pp
stringendo
rallent.
gneur, sois bé - ni dans le Sei-gneur! Jean! ah! sois bé-
fall, May heav'n's choicest blessing fall, Jean! ah! May heav'n bless thee
ni!
now!
dolce
sempre
dimin.
pp

Donnez, donnez

Romance

from "Le Prophète"

English version by
H. Millard

Giacomo Meyerbeer
(1791 - 1864)

dolce
dis! Donnez, donnez à
heav'n! Give alms! give alms, or
cresc.
p
Ped.
la pauvre femme Qui prie, hélas! qui prie, hélas! pour son
one more will perish Who prays, alas! who prays, alas! her son to
rall.
fils! Donnez, donnez, noble seigneur, donnez de grâce au
save. Give alms, give alms, O noble sir, give alms to her, Oh,
a tempo
sein de votre richesse, pitié, seigneur opu
give, of thy wealth bestowing, And pity, sir, no longer
pp
cresc.
dim.
lent! Donnez pour dire une messe, hélas! à mon pauvre en
shun, Relieve my heart overflowing, Alas! for my darling

cresc.
fant, hé - las! à mon pauvre en - fant, hé - las, hé -
son! a - las! for my dar - ling son! A - las! a -
cresc.
dim.
rp
(weeping)
cresc.
ah! ah! ah!
las! à mon pauvre en - fant! ah! ah! ah!
las! for my dar - ling son!
fp
pp
p
cresc.
(weeping)
pi - tié! don - nez! ah! ah! ah! hé - las! pi -
Thy boun - ty give, ah! ah! ah! A - las, for
p
cresc.
tié!
me.
f poco accel.
fp
smorz.
fp
smorz.
J'ai faim, j'ai froid! n'im - por - te! La
I thirst, I'm cold! what mat - ters! The
fp
smorz.
fp
smorz.
ff

tombe est plus froide en - cor! Et moi, bien-tôt
tomb is more chill and lone! And I ere long
col canto
marcato
smorz.
poco accel.
glace-e et morte, Qui donc prie-ra pour son
will there re-pose. Who then will pray for my
sort? qui donc prie-ra pour son sort?
son? who then will pray for my son?
accel.
rall.
dim.
qui donc prie-ra, qui donc prie-ra pour lui, qui donc? Au-
who then will pray, who then will pray for him, who then? Oh,
a tempo
molto dolce
cresc.
sein de vo-tre ri-ches-se, Pi-tié, sei-gneur o-pu-lent! Don-
give, of thy wealth be-stow-ing, And pit-y, sir, no long-er shun, Re-
dim.

dim.
nez pour dire u-ne mes-se, hé-las! à mon pauvre en-fant! hé-
lieve my heart o-ver-flowing, A-las! for my dar-ling son! A-
molto cresc.
f dim. pp
las! à mon pauvre en-fant! hé-las! hé-las! à mon pauvre en-
las! for my dar-ling son! a-las! a-las! for my dar-ling
cresc.
fp
pp
(weeping)
cresc.
(weeping)
fant! Ah! ah! ah! pi-tié! don-nez! Ah! ah! ah! hé-las!
son! Ah! ah! ah! thy boun-ty give! Ah! ah! ah! a-las!
cresc.
p
pi-tié!
for me!
pi-tié!
for me!
p

Gerechter Gott

Recitative and Aria
from "Rienzi"

Richard Wagner
(1813 - 1883)

*The role of Adriano, son of Stefano Colonna, was written for a mezzo-soprano.

a piacere
Er - - de, nimm' mich Jam - - mer-vol-len auf!
Heav'n! a - vert from me this fear-ful sight!
ff
mf
f
f
agitato
agitato sempre
Wo giebt's ein
Hor - ri - ble
f
Schick - - sal das dem mei - - nen gleicht?
thoughts my wand'ring mind dis - tress;
pp
Wer liess mich
Come, Death, and
f
dir ver-fal-len, finst - - re Macht? Ri-
bring to this poor heart re-lief. Ri-
pp
p
f

ff
en - zi, Un - heil-vol - ler! Welch ein Loos
en - zi, Thou am-bi - tious, see thy works!
f 3
ff
a piacere
beschwurst du auf dies un - glücksel - 'ge Haupt?
All Rome by thee is cast in mournful gloom,
colla parte
f
p
cresc.
mf
Wo - hin wend' ich die ir - ren Schritte? Wohin das
This new blood - shed she'll deep - ly sor-row. Thy ray be -
f
fp
cresc.
f
Schwert, des Rit - ters Zier?
stow, O boun - teous Lord!
f
p
Più tranquillo ed espress.
p
f
Wend' ich's auf dich, I - re - nen's Bru-der? zieh' ich's auf mei-nes Va - ters
My soul per - plexed ad-vice would bor-row, Du - ty or love shall have my
f

Andante
Haupt?
sword?
p
espress.
p
più p
espress.
p
molto espress.
p
In sei - ner Blü - the
O dreams of youth, so
p
bleicht mein Le-ben, da-hin, da - hin ist all mein Rit-ter-thum, der Tha - ten Hoffnung
dear, so tender, A - way, a - way, sweet visions of past time; All bliss - ful hopes I
a piacere
ist ver-lo - ren, mein Haupt krönt nimmer, krönt nimmer Glück und Ruhm. Mit
must sur-ren-der, My life doth wither, doth with-er in its prime! Would
p

trü - bem Flor um - hül - let sich mein
but one star now break with light The
Stern im er - sten Ju - gendglanz, durch düst - re Glu - then
aw - ful gloom of this dark night! Love, Love him - self, that
pp
drin - get selbst der schönsten Lie - be Strahl in's Herz. Mit trü - bem
swayed my breast, Now crushed by grief this heart hath left! Would but one
poco cresc.
pp
cresc.
dim.
Flor um-hüllt mein Stern sich im er - sten Ju - gend - glanz, durch düst - re
star now break with light The gloom of this dark night! Love, Love him-
fp
p
Glu - then drin - get selbst der schönsten Lie - be, der schön - sten
self, that swayed my breast, by grief now con - quered by grief now
fp
dolce
p
pp

un poco ritard.
Lie - be Strahl in's Herz, der schön - sten Lie - - be Strahl in's
con - quered, me — hath left! by grief — now con - - quered, me — hath
colla parte
pp
pp
Herz.
left!
p espress.
In sei - ner Blü - the
O dreams of youth, so
a tempo
p
cresc.
fp
bleicht mein Le - ben, da - hin, da - hin ist all mein Rit - ter - thum, der
dear, — so ten - der, A - way, a - way, sweet vi - sions of past time! All
cresc.
rall.
Tha - ten Hoff - nung ist ver - lo - - ren, mein Haupt krönt
bliss - ful hopes I must — sur - ren - - der, My life — doth
p
p dim. e rall.
mezza voce
a tempo
nim - - - - mer Glück und Ruhm! mein Haupt krönt
with - - - - er — in — its prime, my life doth
pp
dolce
col canto
p a tempo
cresc.

nim - mer, ach! nim - mer Glück und Ruhm, mein Haupt krönt
with - er, ah! with - er in its prime, my life doth
nim - mer, ach! nimmer Glück und
with - er, ah! with-er in its
Ruhm, mein Haupt krönt nim - - mer Glück und Ruhm!
prime, my life doth with - - er in its prime!
Allegro
(The bell of the Capitol is heard tolling.)

ff
mf
Wo war ich?
Where am I?
f molto agitato
Ha! wo bin ich jetzt? die
Ah, what now to do? That
ff
f
Glo - cke!
sig - nal!
Gott, es wird zu
Heav'n! what aw - ful
più cresc.
sempre cresc.
spät! Was nun be - gin - - - nen?
sound! The time is fly - - - ing!
sempre cresc.
Ha! nur Eins! hin - aus zum
Du - ty bids, yes, to my
ff
mf

Va- -ter will ich flieh'n! Ver-
fa- -ther I must go! With
söh- -nung glückt viel-leicht dem
him I'd fain to-day be
Sohne,- er muss mich hö-ren, denn sein Knie um-fas-send, ster-
conquered, and per-ish rath-er than a shame- -ful vic-t'ry with
-be wil- -lig ich! Auch der Tri
his foes to share! Yet, if his
bun wird mil- -de sein; in Frie-
heart to peace in-clines, then, Tri-
a piacere
animato
cresc.

- den wandl'ich glüh'n - den Hass! Du
- bune, thou must yield to me! O
molto cresc.
ff
cresc.
Ped.
Maestoso
grandioso
Gna - den-gott, zu dir fleh' ich, der Lieb' in je - der Brust ent -
God of mer - cy, God of peace, Hear thou my pray'r, from ven-geance
ff
mf
flammt! Mit Kraft und Se-gen waff - ne mich, Ver -
cease! Ce - les - tial spi - rit, now de-scend, And
söh-nung sei mein hei-lig Amt.
make their hearts in con-cord blend!
Vivace
con anima
Mit Kraft und Se - gen
Ce - les - tial spi - rit,
f
p molto animato
cresc.
waff - ne mich! Ver - söh - - - - nung
now de-scend, And make their
cresc.

sei mein hei-lig Amt! Mit Kraft und Se - gen waff - ne
hearts in _ con-cord blend! Ce-les - tial spi - rit, now de-
mich, Ver-söh - - nung sei mein hei - lig Amt, Ver-
scend, And make their hearts in con - cord blend, and
molto
cresc.
cresc.
a piacere
söh - nung sei mein hei - lig Amt!
make their hearts in con - cord blend!

Cara sposa, amante cara

Aria

from "Rinaldo"

cresc.
deh! ri - tor - na a' pian - ti mie - i!
Ah! for - sak - en, dear one, I per - ish!
f
Ca - ra spo - sa, a - man - te
Wife be - lov - ed, thou whom I
ca - ra, do - ve se - i? Ri - tor - na, ri - tor - na a'
cher - ish, Say, where art thou? For - sak - en, for - sak - en, dear
pian - ti mie - i, ca - ra spo - sa,
one, I per - ish! Wife be - lov - ed,

deh! ri - tor - na, deh! ri - tor - na a'pian - ti mie -
Ah, for - sak - en, ah, for - sak - en, dear one, I per -
i, ca - ra spo - sa, spo - sa ca - ra, do - ve
ish! Wife be - lov - ed, wife be - lov - ed, Say, where
cresc.
se - i? Deh! ri - tor - na, do - ve sei, do - ve
art thou? Ah! for - sak - en! where art thou, where art
cresc.
sei? deh! ri - tor - na a' pian - ti mie - i, ri - tor - na a'
thou? Ah, for - sak - en, dear one, I per - ish, I shall for -

pian - - - - - ti_ mie - i, deh! ri -
sak - - - - - en_ per - ish! Ah, for -
tor-na, deh! ri - tor-na a' pian - ti_ mie - i
sak-en, ah, for - sak - en, dear one, I per - ish!
f
f
Allegro (non tanto)
p
Del vostro E - re - bo sul - l'a - ra, col - la fa - ce del mio
On your fie - ry moun-tain's al - tars, In dis - dain - ful in - dig -
p

sde-gno io vi sfi-do, col-la fa-ce del mio sdegno io vi sfi-do, o
na-tion, I de-fy ye, in dis-dain-ful in-dig-na-tion I de-fy ye, O
spir-ti re - i! col-la fa-ce del mio sde-gno, del vo-
race in-fer - nal! In dis-dain-ful in-dig-na-tion, on your
stro E-re - bo sul-l'a-ra io vi sfi-do, io vi sfi-do, o
fie-ry moun-tain's al-tars, I de-fy ye, I de-fy ye, O
spir-ti re - i, o spir-ti re i!
race in-fer - nal, O race in-fer nal!
Da Capo al Fine.

Que fais-tu, blanche tourterelle

Chanson

from "Roméo et Juliette"

English version by
Dr. Theodore Baker

Charles Gounod
(1818-1893)

lets À ma voix ce ma-tin o-se-ront re-pa-raî - tre!
lets, If you dare walk a-broad to re-pair your dis-as - ter!
p
Allegretto ♩=88
f
f
f
Poco meno mosso ♩=72
Que fais tu, blan-che tour-te-
Dain-ty dove, where-fore art thou
p
rel - le, Dans ce nid de vau-tours? Quel-que
ly - ing In a wild vul-ture's nest? Soon or

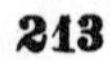

jour, dé - ploy-ant ton aî - le, Tu sui-vras les_ a-
late, far shalt thou be fly - ing, Foll'-wing love's own be-
Ped. * Ped. *
poco animato
mours! Aux vau-tours, il faut la ba-tail - le, Pour frap-
hest! For the vul - tures would fain be fight - ing, And their
p poco animato
per d'e-stoc et de tail - le, Leurs becs sont ai - gui-
beaks are whet - ted for smit - ing; Full sharp are they, and
Tempo I°
sés! Lais - se là ces ois - eaux de proi - e, Tour - te-
strong! Fly a - way, then, from birds of prey, love! Thou wert
ten.
ten.
p
Ped. *

rit.
rel - le qui fais ta joi - e Des a - mou - reux bai -
made on - ly to re - pay, love, Fond kiss - es warm and
rit. pp
Andantino ♩ = 66
sers! Gar - dez bien la bel - le! Qui vi - vrà ve -
long! Guard ye well her dwell - ing, They who live shall
p
pp
drà! Vo - tre tour - te - rel - le Vous é - chap - pe -
see! For your dain - ty dar - ling May one day go
p
ra, Vo - tre - tour - te - rel - le Vous é - chap - pe -
free, For your dain - ty dar - ling May one day go
pp

Tempo I°
ra! Un ramier, loin du vert bocage, Par l'amour attiré, A l'entour de ce nid sauvage A, je crois, soupiré! Les vautours sont à la curée, Leurs chan-
free! Drawn by love, from his woodland hieing, Came a ring-dove that way, All around yonder eyrie sighing He did rove, so they say! Lured a-field by a prey they're mangling, Yet a-
pp
poco animando
p poco animando

sons que fuit Cy - thé - ré - e Ré - son - nent à grand
far the vul - tures are wran - gling, Their cries the ear af -
a tempo
bruit! Ce - pen - dant, en leur douce i - vres - se, Nos a -
fright! And the while, fond - ly won in woo - ing, Lov - ers
a tempo
mants con - tent leur ten - dres - se Aux as - tres de la
twain ten - der - ly are coo - ing 'Neath won - d'ring stars of
pp
Andantino
nuit! Gar - dez bien la bel - le,
night! Guard ye well her dwell - ing!
p
pp

Qui vi - vrà ve - drà! Vo - tre tour - te - rel - le
They who live shall see! For your dain - ty dar - ling
p
Vous é - chap - pe - ra, Vo - tre tour - te - rel - le Vous é -
May one day go free, For your dain - ty dar - ling May one
pp
Più lento
chap - pe - ra! Gar - dez bien la bel - le, Vo - tre tour - te -
day go free! Guard ye well her dwell - ing, For your dain - ty
p
f
tr
rel - le Vous é - chap - pe - ra!
dar - ling May one day go free!
f
ff

Printemps qui commence

Aria
from "Samson et Dalila"

English version by
Nathan Haskell Dole

Camille Saint-Saëns
(1835 - 1921)

16362

â - me, Et ta dou - ce flam - - me Vient sé - cher nos
glad-ness, For Spring's mys-tic mad - - ness Thrills through all the
pleurs; Tu rends à la ter - re, Par un doux mys - tè - - - - re,
earth; She spreads o'er the mead-ows Warm rays, cool-ing shad - - - - ows,
cresc.
Les fruits et les fleurs. En vain je suis bel - le! Mon cœur plein d'a-
Joy, and gen - tle mirth. In vain I a - dorn me With blos - soms and
Ped.
mour, Pleu - rant l'in - fi - dèle, At - tend son re - tour! Vi -
charms, My false love doth scorn me And flees from my arms! But

cresc.
vant d'es-pé-ran-ce, Mon coeur dé-so-lé Gar-de sou-ve-
hope still ca-ress-es My des-o-late heart, Past de-light yet
sf
nan-ce Du bon-heur pas-sé!
bless-es, Love will not de-part.
sf
f
p
dolce
À la nuit tom-ban-te J'i-rai, triste a-
When night comes star-la-den, A sad, lone-ly
dim.
pp
man-te, M'asseoir au tor-rent, L'attendre en pleu-rant! Chas-
maid-en I'll sit by the stream, And, weep-ing, I'll dream. My

cresc.
sant ma tris - tes - se, S'il revient un jour, À lui ma ten - dres -
heart I'll sur - ren - der, Should he come to - day, And still be as ten -
poco cresc.
accel. dim. rit.
se Et la douce i - vres - se Qu'un brû - lant a - mour Garde à
der As when love's first splen - dor Made me rich and gay: So I'll
mf
pp
rit.
Un poco più lento ♩=72 dolce
son re - tour. Chassant ma tris - tes - se,
'wait him al - way! My heart I'll sur - ren - der,
espr.
S'il re - vient un jour, À lui ma ten -
Should he come to - day, And still be as

sempre più p
dres - se! À lui ma ten - dres - se Et la douce i -
ten - der, and still be as ten - der As when love's first
pp
vres - se Qu'un brû - lant a - mour Garde à son re -
splen - dor Made me rich and gay: So I'll 'wait him al -
rit.
r.h.
Più lento
tour!
way!
Ped.

Amour, viens aider

Recitative and Aria

from "Samson et Dalila"

English version by
Nathan Haskell Dole

Camille Saint-Saëns
(1835 - 1921)

16362

Moderato ♩=92
fai - re nos dieux!
soon glo - ri - fy!
cresc.
f
dim.
p
A - mour! viens ai - der ma fai - bles - se!
O Love, of thy might let me bor - row!
Ver - se le poi - son dans son sein!
Pour thy poi - son through Sam - son's heart!
Fais que, vain-
Let him be
f
p

cu par mon a - dres - se, Sam - son soit en - chaî - né — de -
bound be - fore the mor - row, A cap - tive to my match - less
main!
art!
Il voudrait en vain — de son â - me Pou -
In his soul he no long - er would cher - ish The
cresc.
dim.
p
3
voir me chasser, me ban - nir! Pourrait - il é - tein - dre la
pas - sion he wish - es were dead; Can a flame like that ev - er
flam - me Qu'a - li - men - te le sou - ve - nir? Il est à
per - ish, Ev - er - more by remembrance fed? He rests my
pp

moi! c'est mon es - cla - - ve! Mes frè - res
slave; his feats be - lie him! My breth - ren
accel.
cresc.
crai - gnent son courroux; Moi seule en - tre
fear with vain a - larms, I on - ly, of
accel.
cresc.
f a tempo
tous, je le bra - - - - -
all, I de - fy
a tempo
f
ve, Et le re - tiens à mes ge - noux!
him, I hold him fast with - in my arms!
cresc.

A - mour! viens ai-der ma fai -
O Love, of thy might let me
bles - - se! Ver - se le poi - son dans son
bor - - row! Pour thy poi-son through Sam-son's
sein! Fais que, vain - cu par mon a -
heart! Let him be bound be-fore the
dres - - se, Sam - son soit en-chaî - né — de -
mor - - row, A cap - tive to my match - less

dolce
main! Con-tre l'a-mour sa force est
art! When love con-tends, strength ev-er
vai-ne; Et lui, le fort par-mi les
fail-eth; E'en he, though strong-est of the
forts, Lui, qui d'un peu-ple rompt la
strong, Through whom in war his tribe pre-
chaî-ne, Succom-be-ra sous mes ef-forts!
vail-eth, Will'gainst my charms not bat-tle long!
pp

Mon coeur s'ouvre à ta voix

Aria
from "Samson et Dalila"

English version by
Nathan Haskell Dole

Camille Saint-Saëns
(1835 - 1921)

so that better my tears dry up, That your voice
dim.
pour mieux sé-cher mes pleurs, Que ta voix
That my tears no more show - er, Tell thy love
pp
speak's still! Tell
rinf.
parle en-co - re! Dis-
still unshak - en! O
espr.
ME that to Dalila you will never return
moi qu'à Da-li - la tu re-viens pour ja -
say thou wilt not now leave De - li - lah a -
sf
p
pp
Repeat for my pleasure the ex-
rinf.
mais, Re-dis à ma ten-dres - se Les ser-
gain! Re-peat thine ac-cents ten - der, Ev-'ry
sf
p

string.
cresc.
ments d'au-tre-fois, ces ser-ments que j'ai-
pas- - sion-ate vow, O thou dear - est of
string.
mf rit.
Un poco più lento
dolce
mais! Ah! ré-
men! Ah! to the
mf rit.
pp
ponds à ma tendres - se, Ver - se-
charms of love sur-ren - der, Rise with
moi, ver-se-moi l'i-vres - se! Réponds à ma ten-
me to its heights of splen - dor! To love's delights sur-
cresc.

piu cresc.
f con espansione
dres - se, Ré-ponds à ma ten-dres - se! Ah! ver-se -
ren - der, to love's delights sur-ren - der! Ah! rise with
cresc.
dim.
moi, ver-se-moi l'i - vres - se!
me to its heights of splen - dor!
p molto espr.
ff
dim.
Tempo I
pp
dolce
Ain - si qu'on
As fields of

SEES So THE EARS of WHEAT EARS of GRAIN SWAY-
voit des blés les é - pis on-du-
grow - ing corn In the morn bend and
ING UNDER THE light BREEZE
ler Sous la bri - - -
sway, When the light
se lé-gè - re,
zeph-yr ris - es,
Thus MY HEART QUIVERS
Ain - si fré-mit mon coeur,
E'en so my heart for - lorn

READY TO CONSOLE ITSELF
prêt à se con-so-ler,
Is thrilled by pas-sion's play
AT YOUR VOICE WHICH IS DEAR TO ME!
À ta voix qui m'est chè - re!
At thy voi - ce's sweet sur-pris - es!
THE ARROW IS LESS RAPID
rinf. poco animato
La flè - che est moins ra-
Less rap - id is the
sf
pide à por - ter le tré -
dart In its death - deal - ing

Than it is (for) your love
rinf.
pas, Que ne l'est ton a-
flight Than I spring to de-
sf
to fly in your arms!
string.
man- te à vo-ler dans tes bras!
light To my place on thy heart!
string.
cresc.
mf rit.
À vo-ler dans tes bras!
To my place on thy heart!
mf
rit.
Un poco più lento
Ah! reply to my tender thoughts
dolce
Ah! ré - ponds à ma ten-dres - se,
Ah! to love's de - lights sur-ren - der,
p

Ver - se - moi, ver-se - moi l'i - vres - se!
Rise with me to its heights of splen - dor!
cresc.
più cresc.
Ré-ponds à ma ten-dres - se, Ré-ponds à ma ten-dres - se!
To love's delights sur-ren - der, to love's delights sur-ren - der!
cresc.
f
con espansione
p
Ah! verse-moi, verse-moi l'i-vres - se! Samson!
Ah! rise with me to its heights of splen - dor! Samson!
f
dim.
p molto espr.
Samson! je t'ai - me!
Samson! I love thee!
dim.
pp

In sì barbara

Aria

from "Semiramide"

English version by
C. L. Kenney

Gioacchino Rossini
(1792 - 1868)

il mio pian - to, il mio pian - to, il mio do -
Con - so - la - tion, con - so - la - tion let me
lor, il mio do - lor,
gain, ah, let me gain,
il mio do - lor! A que - st'a - ni - ma smar -
ah, let me gain! To the soul with woe con -
ri - ta, Por - gi tu confor - to, a - i - ta. Di mie
tend - ing, Gent - ly aid and com - fort lend - ing, Now a -
pe - ne al cru - do ec - ces - so,
bate the tor - ment rend - ing
ff
pp
ff
p

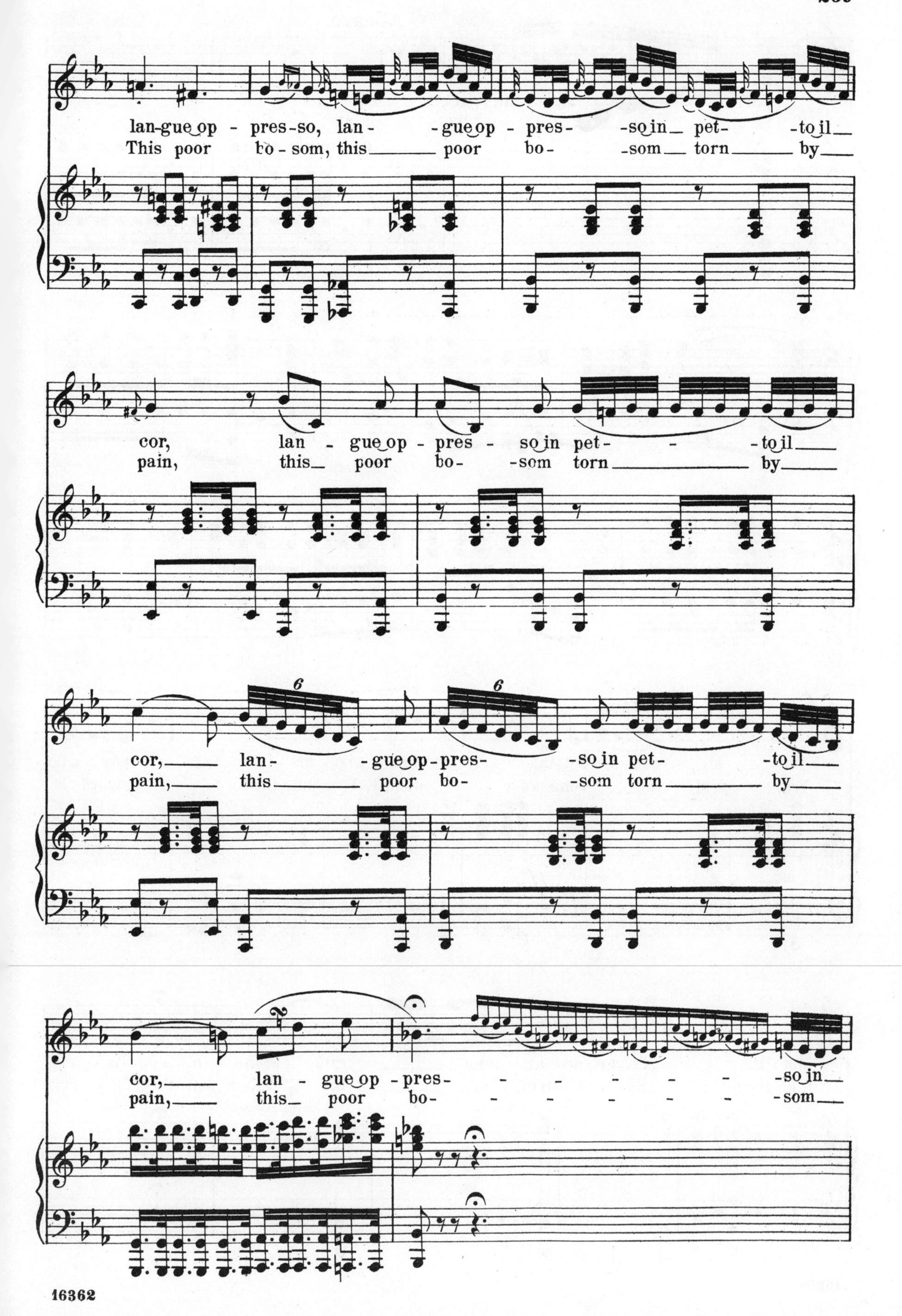
lan-gue op - pres-so, lan - gue op - pres - so in pet - to il
This poor bo-som, this poor bo - som torn by
cor, lan - gue op - pres - so in pet - to il
pain, this poor bo - som torn by
cor, lan - gue op - pres - so in pet - to il
pain, this poor bo - som torn by
cor, lan - gue op - pres - - - - - - so in
pain, this poor bo - - - - - - som

Allegro
pet- - - - -to il cor.
torn so by pain!
Sì, sì, ven - det-ta! por - gi-o - ma - i, por - gi-o -
Yes, yes! for vengeance, sword, I take thee, sword, I
ma - i!.. Sa-cro ac-ciar del ge - ni - to - re, Tu ri-
take thee! Sa-cred steel! my fa - ther bore thee, Thou my

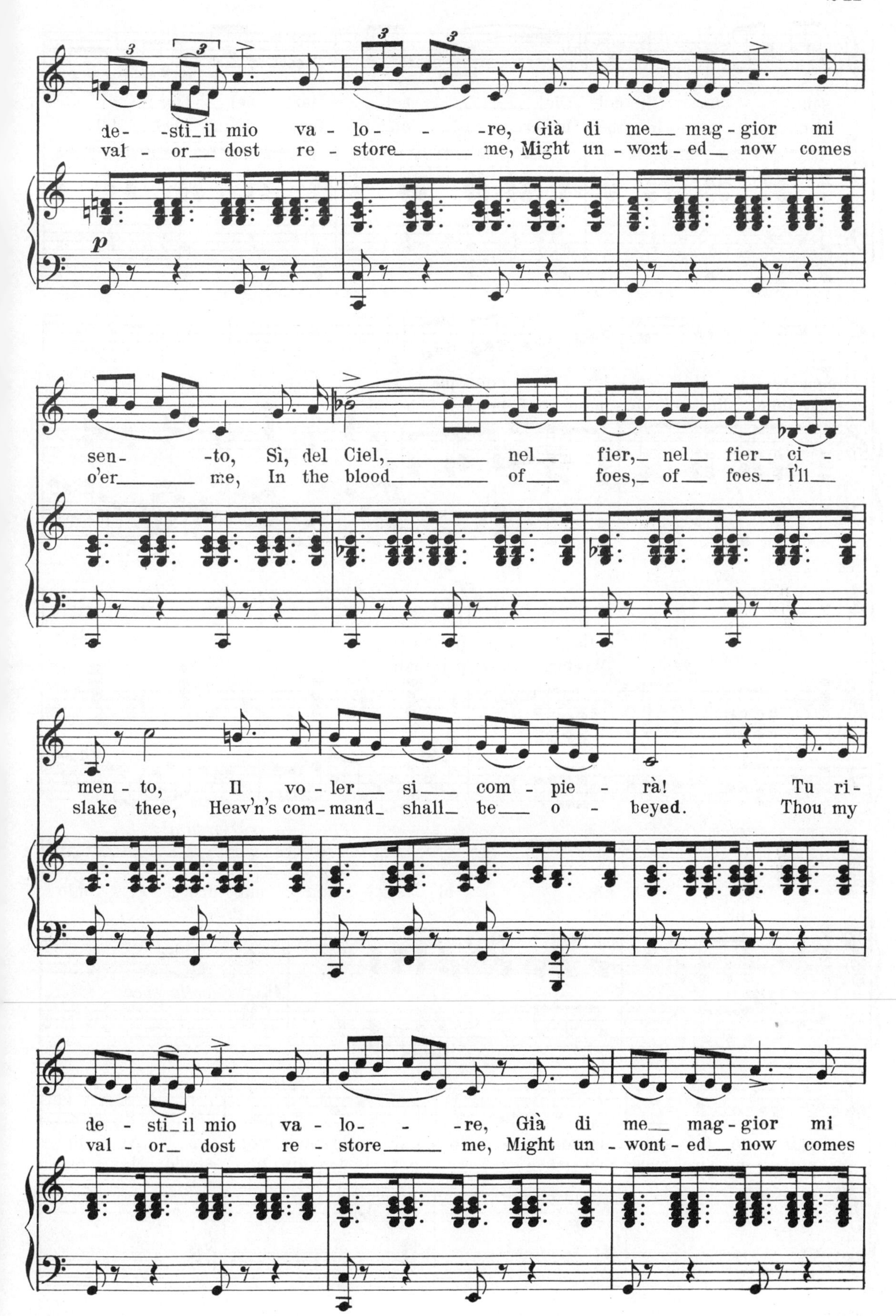
de- -sti_il mio va- lo- -re, Già di me_ mag-gior mi
val - or_ dost re - store_ me, Might un - wont - ed_ now comes
p
sen- -to, Sì, del Ciel,_ nel_ fier,_ nel_ fier_ ci -
o'er_ me, In the blood_ of_ foes,_ of_ foes_ I'll_
men - to, Il vo- ler_ si_ com - pie - rà! Tu ri-
slake thee, Heav'n's com-mand_ shall_ be_ o - beyed. Thou my
de - sti_il mio va- lo- -re, Già di me_ mag-gior mi
val - or_ dost re - store_ me, Might un - wont - ed_ now comes

sen- -to, Sì, del Ciel, nel fier, nel fier- ci-
o'er me, In the blood of foes, of foes I'll
men-to, Il vo-ler- si com-pie-rà.
slake thee, Heav'n's com-mand shall be o-beyed.
ff
Sì, sì! l'em-pio pe-ra!
Yes, yes! Wretch, now per-ish!
ff
pp
f
dolce
rallentando
Ah! ah! el-la è mia ma-dre! Al mio
Ah! ah! she is my moth-er! Mer-cy
pp
p
colla voce
pian-to for-se il pa-dre Per-do-nar-le ancor vor-rà, Al mio
still my sire may cher-ish, Crave I par-don of his shade; Mer-cy

pian - to for-se il pa - dre Per - do - nar - le an-cor vor-rà.
still __ my sire may cher - ish, Crave I par - don be-fore his shade.
Allegro vivace
f
f
con brio
Sì, _ ven-di - ca- -to il _ ge - ni - to- -re, A _ lui sve-
Thy ven-geance sat- -ing, Sire whom I _ cher - ish, Sin ex-pi-
na-to il tra - di - to - re, Pa-ce que - st'a - ni-ma _ sperar po-
at-ing, Thy foe _ shall per - ish, A-gain re - pose-ful calm _ my soul shall
trà, sì, ___ sperar po - trà, ___ sperar po - trà.
know, ay! ___ a-gain shall know, ___ a-gain shall know.

Ai dol-ci pal-pi-ti di
Once more this heart so blest with
gio-ja e a-mo-re, ai dol-ci
pure af-fec-tion, once more this
pal-pi-ti di gio-ja e a-mo-re, Fe-li-ce il
heart so blest with pure af-fec-tion, 'Neath thy pro-
co-re ri-tor-ne-rà, sì, fe-li-ce il
tec-tion Shall fond-ly glow, ay! 'neath thy pro-
cor ri-tor-ne-
tec-tion fond-ly

rà.
glow!
ff
f
Sì! al gran ci - men - to m'af - fret- -to ar-
Yes! for strife pre - par - ing with loft- -y
di - to;
dar - ing,
ff
f
sì, me - co l'As - si - ria re - spi- -re - rà...
Thou free - ly, As - sy - ria, shalt breathe a - gain.
f

Sì,_ ven-di - ca- -to il_ ge - ni-
With ven-geance sat- -ing, Sire whom I_
to- -re, A_ lui_sve - na - to il tra - di - to - re,
cher- -ish, Sin_ex - pi - at - ing, Thy foe_ shall_ per - ish;
Pa-ce quest'a - ni - ma_ spe-rar po - trà, sì,_ sperar po-
A-gain re-pose-ful calm_ my_soul shall know, Ay!_ a-gain shall
trà,_ spe-rar_ po - trà. Ai_
know,_ a - gain shall know. Once_
_ dol - ci pal - pi - ti di_ gio - ja e a -
_ more this heart so_ blest with_ pure af -

mo - re,
fec - tion,
ai dol - ci
once more this
pal - pi - ti di gio - ja e a - mo - re, Fe - li - ce il
heart so blest with pure af - fec - tion, 'Neath thy pro -
co - re ri - tor - ne - rà, sì, fe - li - ce il cor
tec - tion Shall fond - ly glow, ay, 'neath thy pro - tec - -
ff
ri - tor - ne - rà,
tion fond - ly glow,
ff

ri - tor - ne - rà,
shall fond - ly glow,
ri - tor - ne - rà,
shall fond - ly glow,
ri - - tor - - ne - - rà,
shall fond - - ly glow,
ri - tor - ne - rà,
shall fond - ly glow,
ri - tor - ne - rà,
shall fond - ly glow,
ri - - tor - - ne - - rà,
shall fond - - ly glow,
fz
fz

ri - tor - ne - rà, ri -
shall fond - ly glow, shall
tor - ne - rà, ri - tor - ne - rà, ri -
fond - ly glow, shall fond - ly glow, shall
tor - ne - rà, ri - tor - ne - rà!
fond - ly glow, shall fond - ly glow!

Ombra mai fu
Recitative and Aria
from "Serse"

English version by
Mrs. O. B. Boise

George Frideric Handel
(1685 - 1759)

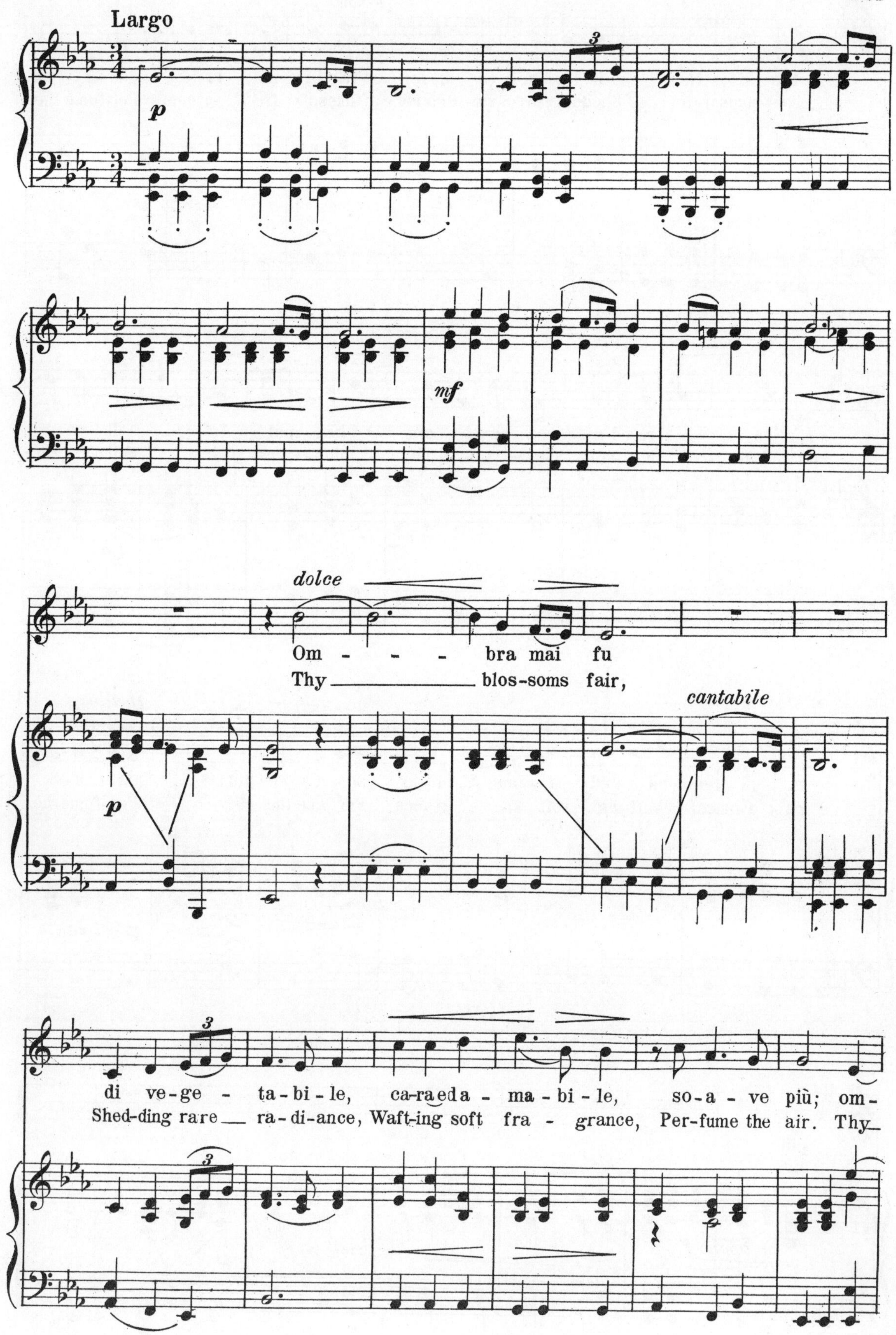
Largo
p
mf
dolce
Om - - - bra mai fu
Thy blos-soms fair,
cantabile
p
di ve-ge - ta-bi-le, ca-ra e da - ma - bi - le, so-a - ve più; om-
Shed-ding rare ra-di-ance, Waft-ing soft fra - grance, Per-fume the air. Thy
3

cresc.
tr
p
-bra mai fu di ve-ge-ta-bi-le, ca-ra ed a-ma-bi-le, so-a-ve
— blos-soms fair, Shedding rare ra-di-ance, Wafting soft fra-grance, Per-fume the
cresc.
p
mf
più, ca-ra ed a-ma-bi-le, om-bra mai fu di ve-ge-
air. Waft-ing soft fra-grance, Thy — blos-soms fair, Shedding rare
mf
p allarg.
3
ta-bi-le, ca-ra ed a-ma-bi-le so-a-ve più, so-a-ve
ra-di-ance, Waft-ing soft fra-grance, Perfume the air, Per-fume the
p col canto

più.
air.
a tempo f
p

Stride la vampa

Aria
from "Il Trovatore"

English version by
Natalia Macfarren

Giuseppe Verdi
(1813 - 1901)

don - na s'a - van - za! Si - ni - stra splen -
girt with her sad - ness. Rough guards with curs -
de sui vol - ti or - ri - bi - li la te - tra
es drag her a - mid the crowd, O'èr all the
fiam - ma che s'al - za, che s'al - za al ciel,
flame rush - es up - ward, ac - cus - ing the sky,
che s'al - za al ciel!
the si - lent sky!
tr
p
f
ff

tr
Stri - de la vam - pa! giun - ge la
Fierce flames are roar - ing, bring forth the
vit - ti - ma ne - ro ve - sti - ta,
sac - ri - fice, Bare - foot, un - gir - dled,
f
di - scin - ta e scal za! Gri - do fe - ro -
in gar - ment sa - ble, Yells of de - ri -
marcato
pp
ce di mor - te le - va - si, l'e - co il ri -
sion greet - ed her ag - o - ny, Wri - thing they

pe - te di bal-za in bal - za! Si -
bound her, 'mid cries as of Ba - bel, And
ni-stra splen - de sui vol - ti or - ri - bi - li
there they watched her scorch at the fie - ry stake,
la te-tra fiam - ma che s'al-za, che s'al-za al ciel,
O'er all the flame rush - es up-ward, ac-cus-ing the sky,
che s'al - za al ciel!
the si - lent sky!
tr
ff

Condotta ell'era in ceppi

Aria
from "Il Trovatore"

English version by
Natalia Macfarren

Giuseppe Verdi
(1813 - 1901)

mar-si e be - ne-dir - mi!
flames her breath could smoth - er!
Chè, fra be-stem-mie o-sce - ne, pun-
Guards, sav-age and fe-ro - cious, With
gen do-la coi fer-ri, al ro-go la cac-cia-va-no gli scel-le-ra-ti
jeers bru-tal-ly load her, With spears and cru-el, taunt-ing words in-to the flames they
sgher-ri;
goad her;
Al-lor, con tron-co ac-cen - to: "mi
And in her dy-ing strug - gle, "A-
ven - di-ca!„ sclа-mo.
venge thou me," she cried:
Quel det - to un e - co e-ter - no in que-sto
Those words I hear for-ev - er wher-e'er I

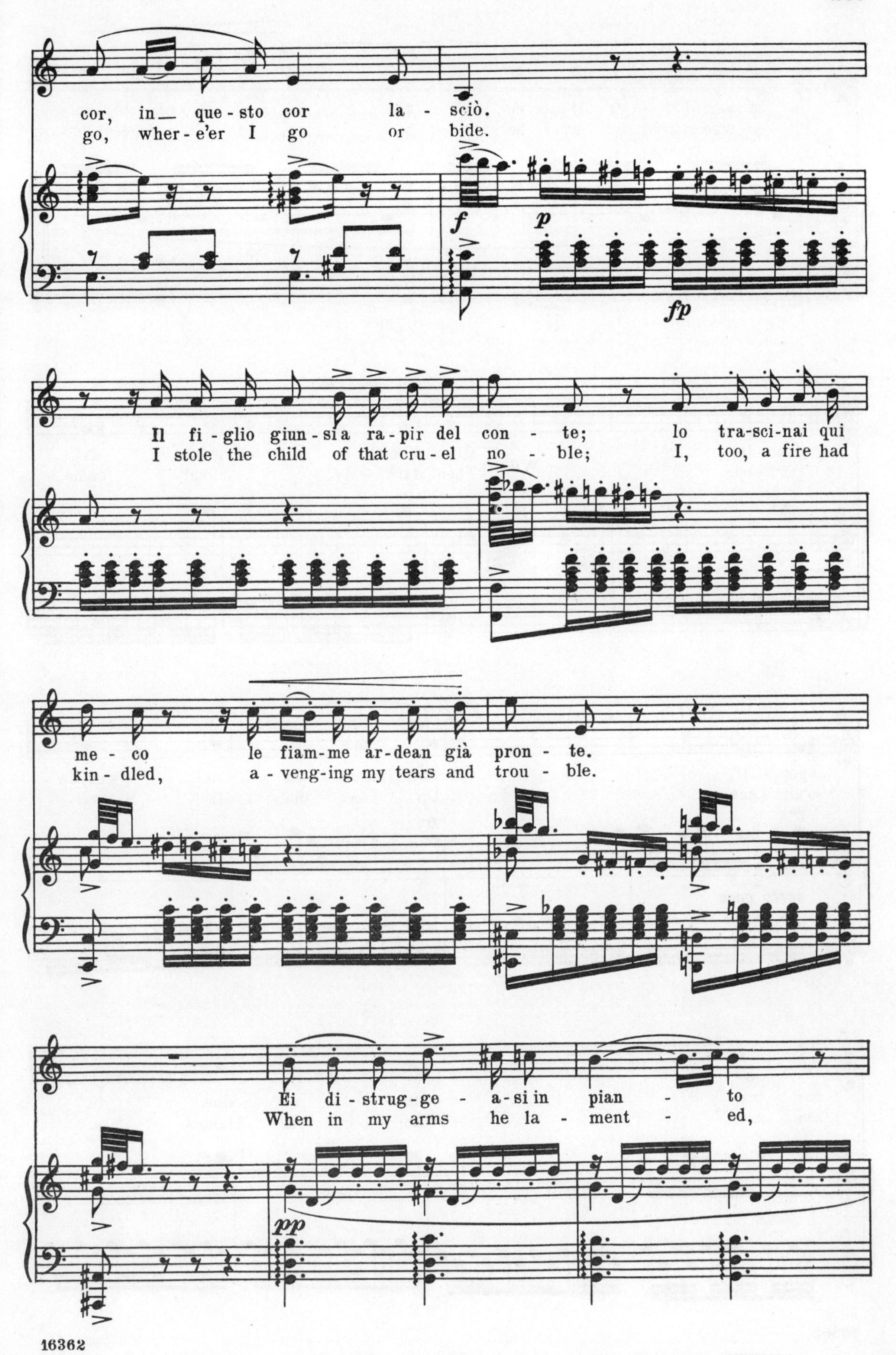
cor, in_ que-sto cor la - sciò.
go, wher-e'er I go or bide.
Il fi-glio giun-si a ra-pir del con - te; lo tra-sci-nai qui
I stole the child of that cru-el no - ble; I, too, a fire had
me-co le fiam-me ar-dean già pron - te.
kin-dled, a-veng-ing my tears and trou - ble.
Ei di-strug-ge - a-si in pian - to
When in my arms he la - ment - ed,

io mi sen - ti - va il co - re di - la - nia - to, in -
Pit - y was stirred in my bo - som, I my pur-pose re -
Allegretto ♩. = 60
sotto voce e declamato
fran - to! Quand'ec - co a - gl'e gri
pent - ed. Then dark - ly a cloud came
pp sempre
ppp
spir - ti, co - me in un so gno, ap -
o'er me, Up - rose that fa - tal.
tr
sotto voce
par - ve la vi - sion fe -
vi - sion. Lu - rid flames a -

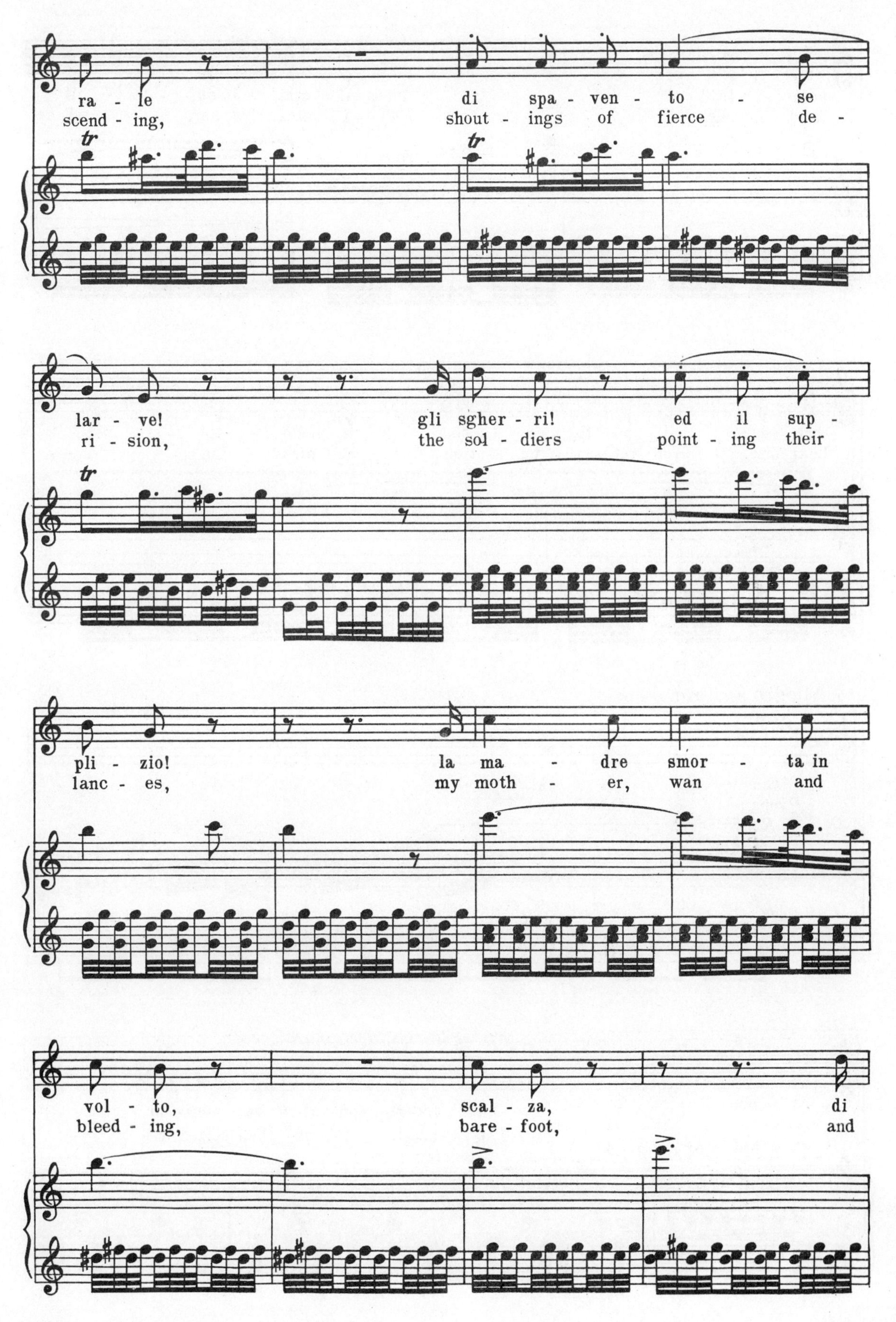
ra - le di spa - ven - to - se
scend - ing, shout - ings of fierce de -
lar - ve! gli sgher - ri! ed il sup -
ri - sion, the sol - diers point - ing their
pli - zio! la ma - dre smor - ta in
lanc - es, my moth - er, wan and
vol - to, scal - za, di
bleed - ing, bare - foot, and
tr

scin - ta!
fainting,
il gri - do, il
I hear her, I
gri - do, il no - to gri - do a - scol - to! "Mi
hear her, for ret - ri - bu - tion she's plead - ing: "A -
Allegro agitato
ven di - ca!,,
venge thou me!"
dim.
pp agitatiss. declamato
La ma - no con - vul - sa sten - do
The shud-der of death then seized me;

strin - go la vit-ti-ma nel fo - co la trag-go,
o - ver her hap-less head the flames rose de-vour-ing,
la so-spin-go! Ces - sa il fa-tal de-
in they drove her! Hor - ror my sens - es
li - rio l'or-ri-da sce-na fug-ge la
cloud - ed, from that dread vi-sion turn-ing, I
fiam - ma sol di-vam-pa, e la sua pre-da
saw the fire be-fore me, my strugg-ling vic-tim
ff
pp

strug-ge! Pur vol-go in-tor - no il guar-do e in-
burn-ing! And when I looked a-round me, in-
ff
pp
p
nan-zi a me veg-g'i-o del-l'em-pio con - te il fi-glio!
stead of him I cher-ished, I saw the ha - ted in-fant!
Il fi-glio mi-o, mio fi-glio a-vea bru-cia - to!
My own had per-ished And I, and I had slain him!
cresc. sempre
ff
Ah!
Ah!

Mio fi - glio, mio fi - glio,
Oh, hor - ror! oh, hor - ror!
fff
il fi - glio mi - o! il fi - glio mi -
My son had per - ished, and I my - self,
8
- o a - vea bru - cia - to!
myself had slain him!
dim.
pp

sempre dim.
Sul ca - po mi - o le chio -
Ah! let me think on that day
allarg. poco a poco e morendo
me sen - to driz - zar - si an - cor! driz -
no more, the re - mem - brance is death I
allarg. poco a poco e morendo
zar - si an - cor! driz - zar - si an - cor!
can no more, I can no more.
allarg. morendo
ppp
pppp

Wo in Bergen du dich birgst

Fricka's Scene
from "Die Walküre"

English version by
Frederick Jameson

Richard Wagner
(1813 - 1883)

Noth, um Ra - che rief er mich an: der E - he Hü - te-rin
cry, for ven-geance called he on me, and wed - lock's guar - dian gave
cresc.
dim.
hör - te ihn ver-hiess streng zu stra-fen die That des frech
ear to him: I made oath to pun-ish the deed of this
fre-veln-den Paar's, das kühn den Gat - ten ge-kränkt. Wie
in-fam-ous pair who rash - ly wrought him a wrong. Thou
dim.
thö - rig und taub_ du dich stellst, als wüss - test führ-wahr du nicht, dass um der
feignst to be fool - ish and deaf, as though thou knew'st not, in sooth, that now for
cresc.

E - he hei - li-gen Eid, den hart ver-letz - ten, ich kla - ge!
wed - lock's ho - ly oath pro-faned so rude - ly, I call thee!
Mässig
Ach-test du rühm-lich der E - he Bruch, so prah - le nun wei-ter und preiss' es
Deem-est thou praise-wor-thy wed-lock's breach, then prate thou yet far-ther and call it
hei - lig, dass Blut schan-de ent-blüht dem Bund ei-nes Zwil-lings-paar's!
ho - ly that shame now blos-som forth from bond of a twin-born pair!
Mir schau-dert das Herz, es schwin-delt mein Hirn: bräut - lich um-fing die
I shud - der at heart, my rea - son doth faint; broth - er em-braced as

Schwe-ster den Bru - der! Wann ward es er-lebt, dass
bride his own sis - ter! When was it e'er known that
ff
Ped.
ff
mf
leib - lich Ge-schwis-ter sich lieb - ten?
broth - er and sis - ter were lov - ers?
cresc.
dolce
Sehr lebhaft
So ist es denn aus mit den
Is all, then, at end with the
p cresc.
ff
e - wig-en Gött - ern, seit du die wil - den Wäl - sun-gen zeug-test?
glo - ry of god-hood since thou be-gatt'st the ri - o-tous Wäl-sungs?
dim.
p
f

Her-aus sagt' ich's traf ich den Sinn? Nichts gilt dir der
I now speak it; pierced is thy thought? Nought worth is to
Heh-ren hei-li-ge Sip-pe! Hin wirfst du Al-les was einst du ge-
thee the race of e-ter-nals! A-way thou cast-est what once thou didst
ach-tet, zer-reis-sest die Ban-de, die selbst du ge-bun-den, lö-sest la-chend des Him-mels
hon-or; thou break-est the bonds thou thy-self hast or-dain-ed, loos-est laugh-ing all heav-en's
Haft: dass nach Lust und Lau-ne nur wal-te diess
hold, that in wan-ton free-dom may flour-ish this
mf
f
cresc.
ff
p

fre-veln-de Zwil - lings-paar, dei-ner Un-treu-e zucht-lo-se Frucht.
in-so-lent twin - born pair, of thy false-ness the un-ho-ly fruit.
cresc.
più p
p
O was klag' ich um E-he und Eid, da zu-
O why wail I o'er wed-lock and vows which thy-
f
f dim.
p
erst du selbst sie ver-sehrt. Die treu - e Gat-tin tro-gest du
self thou first hast pro-faned. The tru - est wife thou still hast be-
sf
f
dim.
stets; wo ei-ne Tie - fe, wo ei-ne Hö - he, da-hin lug - te lü-stern dein
trayed; nev-er a deep and nev-er a height, but there turned thirst-ing ev-er thy
sf
cresc.
f
dim.
p dolce
sf

Blick, wie des Wech-sels Lust du ge-wän-nest, und höh-nend kränkt-est mein
looks, as thy change-ful hu-mour al-lured thee, and stung my heart with thy
tr
tr
tr
Herz. Trau - ern-den Sin-nes musst ich's er-
scorn. Sad - dened in spir-it, must I be-
cresc.
f
dim.
p
tra-gen, zogst du zur Schlacht mit den schlim-men Mäd-chen, die wil - der Min - ne Bund dir ge-
hold thee fare to the fight with the grace-less maid-ens, whom law - less love hath giv-en to
p
bar: denn dein Weib noch scheut-est du so, dass der Wal-kür-en Schaar, und Brünn-hil - de
thee: for thy wife still fear-edst thou so, that the Val-kyr-ies' band and Brünn-hild' her-
p
p

selbst, dei-nes Wun-sches Braut, in Ge-hor-sam der Her-rin du
self, thine own wish-'s bride, to the god-dess as hand-maids thou
fp
gabst. Doch jetzt, da dir neu-e Na-men ge-fie-len, als
gav'st. But now, when un-wont-ed names have en-snared thee, as
p
p
„Wäl-se" wölf-isch im Wal-de du schweif-test; jetzt, da zu nied-rig-ster Schmach du dich neig-test, ge-
"Wal-se" wolf-ish in woods thou hast wan-dered; now that to deep-est dis-grace thou hast fall-en, to
p
mei-ner Men-schen ein Paar zu er-zeu-gen: jetzt dem Wur-fe der Wöl-fin
fos-ter mor-tals be-got of thy false-ness: shamed by whelps of a wolf thou
p
p
cresc.

wirfst du zu Füs - sen dein Weib!
flingst at thy feet, too, thy wife!
più f
So führ' es denn aus! Fül - le das Mass!
Then fin - ish thy work! Fill now the cup!
ff
f
Die Be - trog' - ne lass auch zer - tre - ten!
The be - trayed one tram - ple be - neath thee!
dim.
p

Va! laisse couler mes larmes

Aria

from "Werther"

English version by
Lorraine Noel Finley

Jules Massenet
(1842 - 1912)

Un peu animé
rall.
dim.
mf
pa - ti - en-tes gout-tes Mar - tè - lent le cœur triste et las! Sa ré-sis-tan - ce
drops for-ev-er beat-ing A sor - row-ful heart, held in thrall. And thus re-sist - ant,
p
suivez
dol.
en-fin s'é-pui - se; Le cœur se creuse et s'af-fai-blit...
with grief un-spo - ken, The heart is weak, tired out by woe.
pp
p en animant
Ier Mouvt.
Il est trop grand, rien ne l'em - plit; Et trop fra -
So deep a well will not o'er - flow; Too frail a
r.h.
ff
sf
f
gi - le, tout le bri - se... Tout le bri - se!
heart is crushed and bro - ken, crushed and bro - ken.
ppp
pp